Fire Department Company Officer

Second Edition

VALIDATED BY

**INTERNATIONAL FIRE SERVICE
TRAINING ASSOCIATION**

PUBLISHED BY
**FIRE PROTECTION PUBLICATIONS
OKLAHOMA STATE UNIVERSITY**

Cover Photo Courtesy of: Boone County Missouri Fire District

Dedication

This manual is dedicated to the members of that unselfish organization

of men and women who hold devotion to duty

above personal risk, who count on sincerity of service above

personal comfort and convenience, who strive unceasingly to find

better ways of protecting the lives, homes and property

of their fellow citizens from the ravages of fire and other

disasters ... The Firefighters of All Nations.

Dear Firefighter:

The International Fire Service Training Association (IFSTA) is an organization that exists for the purpose of serving firefighters' training needs. IFSTA is a member of the Joint Council of National Fire Organizations. Fire Protection Publications is the publisher of IFSTA materials. Fire Protection Publications staff members participate in the National Fire Protection Association and the International Society of Fire Service Instructors.

If you need additional information concerning our organization or assistance with manual orders, contact:

For assistance with training materials, recommended material for inclusion in a manual or questions on manual content, contact:

Customer Services
Fire Protection Publications
Oklahoma State University
Stillwater, OK 74078-0118
1-(800) 654-4055

Technical Services
Fire Protection Publications
Oklahoma State University
Stillwater, OK 74078-0118

First Printing, March 1990
Second Printing, November 1990

© *1989 by the Board of Regents, Oklahoma State University*
All rights reserved
ISBN 0-87939-084-0
Library of Congress 89-82071
Second Edition
Printed in the United States of America

Table Of Contents

PREFACE . . . . **ix**
GLOSSARY . . . . **xi**
INTRODUCTION **3**
The Vital Connecting Link: The Company Officer 3
How To Succeed In The Fire Service 5
Today's Company Officer 7

1 PRINCIPLES OF ORGANIZATION **11**
Unity Of Command 12
    Breaches In The Unity-Of-Command Concept 14
Span Of Control 17
Division Of Labor 19
Discipline 21
Summary 22

2 ORGANIZATIONAL STRUCTURE **25**
The Scalar Structure As A Base Of Fire Department Organization 25
Line And Staff 27
    Traditional Staff Advisory 28
    Staff Direct Implementation Method 28
    Undesirable Overlap 30
    Staff Direct Advice 31
    Mutual Staff/Line Overlap 31
    Line Advice To Staff 32
Authority To Implement 32
Company Organizational Structures 34
    The Social Structure 34
    Flat Centralized Organizational Structure 35
    The Scalar Organizational Structure 35
    The Circular Organizational Structure 36
Summary 37

3 COMMUNICATIONS **41**
Communications As A Process 41
    The Sender And Receiver 41
The Message 43
The Medium 43
Listening 45
Formal Communications 46
    Written Policies And Procedures 46
Standard Operating Procedures 48
    Orders And Directives 48
    Fireground Orders 49
Fireground Communications 49
Face-To-Face Communications 51

Officer-Firefighter Relationships 51
Selective Hearing 52
Words Have Different Meanings 52
Emotional Context 53
Physical Barriers 54
Written Communications 54
    The Memorandum 54
    Forms 54
The Letter 55
    Format Of Letters 56
Report Writing 59
Informal Communications 61
    Grapevine 61
Summary 63

4 THE COMPANY AS A GROUP **67**
Group Dynamics 68
    Common Binding Interests 69
    Vital Group Image 70
    Sense Of Continuity 70
    Moral Values 70
    Different Roles Within The Group 71
    The Company Officer's Combination Of Roles 72
    Role Expectation 72
    Rules And Guidelines 73
    The Group As Individuals 73
    Basic Physiological Needs 74
    Safety And Security 74
    Belonging And Social Activity 75
    Esteem And Status 75
    Self-Actualization And Fulfillment 76
    Application Of Maslow's Need Model 76
    Social Need Fulfillment 76
    Esteem And Status Application 77
Transactional Analysis 78
Strokes And Stamp Collecting 80
    Socioeconomic Background As A Group Factor 81
Summary 84

5 LEADERSHIP AS A GROUP INFLUENCE **89**
The Basic Views Of Leadership 89
    Theory X 90
    Theory Y 90
    Theory Z 93
    Bureaucratic Leadership 95
    Single-Issue Leadership 96
    Middle-Of-The-Road Leadership 97
    Dual-Issue Leadership 97
Sizing Up Leadership Styles 98

Dimensions Of Leadership 98
  Making People Feel Strong 99
  Building Trust In The Leader 100
  Cooperating To Achieve Common Goals 101
  Confronting Conflicts Instead Of Running Away 102
Goal Oriented Thinking 103
Power Structures 103
  Reward Power 104
  Coercive Power 104
  Identification Power 104
  Expert Power 104
  Legitimate Power 105
Summary 105

6 ELEMENTS OF MANAGEMENT 109
The Management Cycle 109
Planning 110
Budgeting 111
  The Budgetary Process 112
  Budgetary Controls 113
Organizing 114
  Human Resources 115
  Physical Facilities 115
  Training 115
  Time 115
Implementing 118
  Directing 119
  Controlling 120
Evaluating 120
Goal-Setting Process 122
Long-Range Plans And Goals 122
Medium-Range Plans And Goals 122
Short-Range Plans And Goals 123
Immediate Plans And Objectives 123
Management By Objectives System 124
Setting Objectives In The Management By Objectives Process 125
Summary 125

7 COMPANY MOTIVATION 129
Individual Behavior 130
Affecting Moral And Ethical Influences 131
Affecting Perspectives 132
Affecting Expectations 133
Affecting Needs 135
  Indicators Of High Achievement Needs For Firefighters 136
  Indicators Of High Power Needs For Firefighters 136
  Indicators Of High Affiliation Needs For Firefighters 136
Organizational Tasks As Motivators 136
  Is It An Achievement Task? 137

    Is It A Power Task? 137
    Is It An Affiliation Task? 138
  Combination Of Factors As A Prime Motivator 138
  Summary 138

8 CAREER COUNSELING **143**
  Employee Evaluation 144
    The Basis Of Employee Evaluation 145
    Fire Service Standards 146
    Compatibility Of Performance With Job Requirements 148
  The Evaluation Cycle 150
    Interaction 150
    Dialogue 151
    Behavior Reinforcement 151
    Behavior Modification 152
    Criteria Evaluation 154
  Discipline 155
    Oral Reprimand 155
    Written Reprimand 156
    Transfer 156
    Suspension 157
    Demotion 157
    Termination 157
  Documentation 157
  Evaluation Techniques For Effective Interviews 158
  Coaching Goal-Oriented Behavior 161
  Where Do You Stand? 161
  Summary 162

9 PROBLEM SOLVING **167**
  Problem Recognition 168
  Collecting Data 168
  Analyzing 169
  Developing Alternatives 170
  Selecting The Best Alternative 170
  Implementing The Solution 171
  Monitoring The Results 171
  Taking Corrective Action 172
  Handling Complaints 173
  The Chronic Complainer 175
  Summary 176

10 PRE-INCIDENT SURVEYS **181**
  Considerations When Making The Facility Survey 184
    Fire Control 185
    Property Conservation 189
    Facility Survey Equipment 190
    Systematic Approach 191

Types Of Building Construction 192
    Facility Survey Drawings 192
    The Field Sketch 192
    The Report Drawing 192
    Types Of Drawings 193
    Using Photography 194
Role Of The Company Officer 195
Public Relations 195
Codes And Standards 195
Summary 196

11 FIREGROUND MANAGEMENT **199**
Strategic Plans 199
    In-Service Company Inspections 200
Offensive Fire Attack 201
Defensive Fire Attack 202
    Following Standard Operating Procedures 203
Operational Strategies And Tactics 205
The Tactical Stage 209
Summary 211

12 SIZE-UP **215**
Environmental Considerations 215
Nature Of The Incident 218
The Occupancy 219
Resources 222
Summary 223

13 INCIDENT COMMAND AND COMMUNICATIONS **227**
Radio Communications 228
    Basic Radio Communications 229
Transmission Of Essential Information 230
    Direct Orders 230
    Requests Or Indirect Orders And Directives 231
    Conciseness 232
    Clarity 232
    Confidence 232
    Control 233
    Capability 234
Summary 234

14 FIREFIGHTER SAFETY AND HEALTH **237**
Firefighter Injuries 237
    Sources Of Injuries 238
Stress 240
    Physical, Environmental, and Psychological Stressors 241
    Reducing Physical and Environmental Stress 243
    Psychological Stress—Signals And Reduction 243
    Substance Abuse 244

Critical Incident Stress 245
   Symptoms Of Critical Incident Stress 245
   Reducing Critical Incident Stress (A Posttrauma Program) 247
Training 247
Peer Support 248
Debriefing 248
Counseling 249
Wellness Programs 249
Summary 250

15 COMPANY OFFICER'S LIABILITY **255**
General Principles Of Administrative Law 255
Legal Duty And Liability 258
Bases For Legal Action 259
   Tort Liability 259
   Causation 260
   Negligence 261
   Standard Of Care 261
   Personal Liability 262
   Supervisor's Responsibility For Subordinate's Acts 263
   Summary 263

APPENDIX A—Skills And Personnel Management Model 265

List Of Tables

14.1   Fire Fighter Injuries By Nature Of Injury And Type Of Duty 239

THE INTERNATIONAL FIRE SERVICE TRAINING ASSOCIATION

The International Fire Service Training Association is an educational alliance organized to develop training for the fire service. The annual meeting of its membership consists of a workshop conference which has several objectives —

. . . to develop training material for publication
. . . to validate training material for publication
. . . to check proposed rough drafts for errors
. . . to add new techniques and developments
. . . to delete obsolete and outmoded methods
. . . to upgrade the fire service through training

This training association was formed in November 1934, when the Western Actuarial Bureau sponsored a conference in Kansas City, Missouri, to determine how all agencies that were interested in publishing fire service training material could coordinate their efforts. Four states were represented at this conference and it was decided that, since the representatives from Oklahoma had done some pioneering in fire training manual development, other interested states should join forces with them. This merger made it possible to develop nationally recognized training material which was broader in scope than material published by an individual state agency. This merger further made possible a reduction in publication costs, since it enabled each state to benefit from the economy of relatively large printing orders. These savings would not be possible if each individual state developed and published its own training material.

From the original four states, the adoption list has grown to forty-four American States; six Canadian Provinces; the British Territory of Bermuda; the Australian State of Queensland; the International Civil Aviation Organization Training Centre in Beirut, Lebanon; the Department of National Defence of Canada; the Department of the Army of the United States; the Department of the Navy of the United States; the United States Air Force; the United States Bureau of Indian Affairs; The United States General Services Administration; and the National Aeronautics and Space Administration (NASA). Representatives from the various adopting agencies serve as a voluntary group of individuals who govern policies, recommend procedures, and validate material before it is published. Most of the representatives are members of other international fire protection organizations and this meeting brings together individuals from several related and allied fields, such as:

. . . key fire department executives and drillmasters,
. . . educators from colleges and universities,
. . . representatives from governmental agencies,
. . . delegates of firefighter associations and organizations, and
. . . engineers from the fire insurance industry.

This unique feature provides a close relationship between the International Fire Service Training Association and other fire protection agencies, which helps to correlate the efforts of all concerned.

The publications of the International Fire Service Training Association are compatible with the National Fire Protection Association's Standard 1001, "Fire Fighter Professional Qualifications (1987)," and the International Association of Fire Fighters/International Association of Fire Chiefs "National Apprenticeship and Training Standards for the Fire Fighter." The standards are an effort to attain professional status through progressive training. The NFPA and IAFF/IAFC Standards were prepared in cooperation with the Joint Council of National Fire Service Organizations of which IFSTA is a member.

The International Fire Service Training Association meets each July. Fire Protection Publications at Oklahoma State University publishes all IFSTA training manuals and texts. While most of the IFSTA training manuals can be used for self-instruction, they are best suited to group work under a qualified instructor.

Preface

The second edition of **Fire Department Company Officer** is written for firefighters and driver/operators who desire promotion to the rank of a company officer; for company officers determined to remain versed in essential and innovative management, leadership, and human relations methods; and, for training officers responsible for teaching and developing officers and officer candidates. A knowledge of essential fire fighting skills is assumed.

The objectives listed at the beginning of each chapter parallel the requirements of NFPA 1021, *Fire Officer Professional Qualifications*, for Fire Officer I, II, and III, in personnel and fireground management. The classic supervisory functions of planning, organizing, staffing, directing, and fireground control are discussed. Another area this manual identifies is human relations. Fire officers must know how to communicate; that is, they must be able to listen as well as give direction. In addition, fire officers must be aware of contemporary concerns of human relations such as equal opportunity employment, increased emphasis on professional development, the health and safety of the individuals within their command, and the officer's legal responsibilities to the men and women in the department and the community they serve.

As educational tools, there are two additional resources available that are designed in conjunction with this manual—a student guide and an instructor guide. The student study guide can be used independently of the instructor's guide to identify important concepts and ensure retention; however, it is recommended that all three publications be used simultaneously to obtain the maximum learning experience. The instructor guide should be used by, and is designed for, educators that require the convenience and accuracy of using pre-developed lesson plans with overhead visuals specifically designed to supplement the material covered in this manual.

Acknowledgement and special thanks are extended to the members of the validating committee who contributed their time and wisdom to this manual.

Chairman
Bill Hulsey
Broken Arrow, Oklahoma

Vice-Chairman
George Luther
Meriden, Connecticut

Secretary
Joe Bachtler
Salisbury, Maryland

F. Dan Belanger
Baton Rouge, Louisiana

Gary Girod
Camarillo, California

Bill Meehan
Milford, Nebraska

Jeff Morrissette
Meriden, Connecticut

Randy Novak
Urbana, Illinios

George Tockstein
Santee, California

Ricky Ziebart
East Camden, Arkansas

Special thanks are extended to Katherine Huggins for her artwork throughout this manual, and to Lori Schoonover for her expertise in computer-generated art. The cover photo is courtesy of Boone County, Missouri Fire District.

Photos throughout the publication are through the courtesy and consideration of a number of members of the Edmond, Oklahoma Fire Department. Their assistance is greatly appreciated.

Gratitude is also extended to the following members of the Fire Protection Publications staff, whose contribution made the final publication of this manual possible.

William Westhoff, Senior Publications Editor
Robert P. Fleischner, Publications Specialist
Lynne Murnane, Senior Publications Editor
Carol Smith, Associate Editor
Cynthia Brakhage, Publications Specialist
Susan S. Walker, Instructional Development Coordinator
Don Davis, Publications Production Coordinator
Ann Moffat, Senior Graphic Designer
Lori Schoonover, Graphic Designer
Desa Porter, Graphic Designer
Karen Murphy, Phototypesetting Technician
Terri Jo Gaines, Senior Clerk Typist
Gary Courtney, Research Technician
Jeff Windham, Research Technician
Rick Windham, Research Technician

Gene P. Carlson
Assistant Director

Introduction

Introduction

THE VITAL CONNECTING LINK: THE COMPANY OFFICER

It is 02:48 on a typical December morning. The temperature has been hovering around zero most of the day with a light snow falling. You have been assigned to Engine 5 for only a short time since being promoted to Captain, but have already developed a healthy respect for the area of the city in which it operates. Since turning in around 22:00 last evening, you have been blessed by the communications center with a vehicle fire and two medical emergencies, each sufficiently spaced to allow for 15 or 20 minutes of "quick sleep" between calls.

This time, however, sleep does not come quickly and your mind wanders as you glance around the bunkroom and think about the members of your crew. The engineer assigned to Engine 5 is an "old salt" with six or seven years experience in that slot. Word has it in the department that he could get you water in less than 30 seconds in the middle of the desert. Having concluded the recruit class three years ago, the two firefighters have equal time in the organization. You have had some problems with "teamwork" but you are sure that with time...

That thought process is destroyed with the sounding of the ever-familiar house tones for Station 5. The communications center follows the tones with "Engine 5; Engine 3; Truck 3; Squad 1; Battalion 2; a reported commercial structure fire at Ajax Chemical Company, 111 East High Street. Time out 03:05 KXS 916."

As your rig and the members of your team roll through deserted city streets, your thoughts now are exclusively on the business at hand. You review the pre-incident plan for Ajax Chemical and hope you can remember all the information presented last month by the training division on hazardous materials. You know that you will be the first company in, so you review incident command procedures as you travel. Arriving on the scene, your first radio traffic reflects your initial size-up. "Engine 5 on the scene of a two-story commercial structure; light smoke showing on the first floor from the office area; staging will be at High Street and Center Ave.—Engine 5 is Command."

Typical scenario? Sure it is, and it takes place thousands of times a day in fire departments everywhere. In this situation, and all others, the company officer is that *vital connecting link* between the initial stages and the mitigation of the emergency. The company officer provides the first strategy on which other officers build until the incident is concluded. That foundation is critical and must be done correctly for the situation to be brought to a satisfactory conclusion.

The company officer not only provides that vital link during emergency operations, but also fills the same role in day-to-day activities (Figure I.1). Consider the impact a truly motivated, progressive company officer has in the following departmental activities:

- Use of rules and regulations
- Company management

Figure I.1 The company officer is the vital link during emergency situations and daily activities.

- Pre-incident plan data collection
- Fire company inspections
- Company training evolutions
- Departmental communications
- Company motivation
- Implementing goals and objectives
- Problem solving and career counseling
- Departmental records and reports
- Fireground and fire station safety

The fact is that the company officer plays an important role in the coordination of departmental goals and objectives and, in most instances, is the person who ensures that action is taken to accomplish day-to-day tasks.

Every department must continue to evaluate how it prepares individuals for the all-important position of company officer. One of the major tools used in the training of company officers is this manual: **Fire Department Company Officer.** The goal of this text is to update and expand the material available to further assist those who serve as this "vital connecting link."

HOW TO SUCCEED IN THE FIRE SERVICE

New recruits, upon being introduced to the fire service, are advised of the six basic rules of personal success in the fire service. The company officer should review these rules and apply them with special regard to the company officer's role in the fire service:

Rule 1: *Learn and be sincerely interested in, and dedicated to, your job.* What you are able to contribute to, and receive from, the fire service is limited only by your own degree of personal commitment. Learn to assume responsibility for duties assigned to you. Do your best to analyze and profit by your mistakes and the mistakes of others. Learning from past mistakes will allow you to use your experience and contribute to the effort of the fire company. Fire departments are organized to pool the resources of each company to accomplish departmental goals. Individuals and companies must cooperate so that tasks can be accomplished efficiently and effectively. The company officer must foster this cooperation among the members of the company and with other fire companies.

Rule 2: *Be loyal to the department and to your co-workers.* You are a part of the department, and it is a part of you. Criticism of the department is in fact a criticism of yourself. Strive to understand, and be prepared to defend, the policy and functions of the department. Be constantly aware that you represent yourself, your company, and your department. Your appearance, actions, and manner of conduct are a direct reflection of the fire department. Care and attention should be devoted to preserving a positive image.

Rule 3: *Be aggressive in the pursuit of all education and training opportunities.* Training is an ongoing process throughout your career. The achievement of each educational objective should reveal the path to the ever-increasing body of knowledge with which a company officer is expected to be familiar if he or she is to excel in this challenging profession. Remember that officers function simultaneously at three levels:
— Officers are *students* of the position to which they aspire.
— Officers are *executors* of the position to which they are assigned.
— Officers are *teachers* of those whom they supervise.

Rule 4: *Be cautious. Guard your speech both on and off duty.* As a fire department officer, it is expected that you may possess information that should not be revealed. Handle privileged information as such, but always be willing to discuss the purposes, functions, history, and traditions of the fire service. Since you are expected to be knowledgeable in the areas of fire prevention, fire protection, and fire fighting, be certain that the opinions you express are those of the fire department and are factually correct.

Rule 5: *Be the type of person who inspires confidence and respect.* Do this by being honest, fair, and trustworthy in all your dealings with others and by keeping your personal affairs in such order that they would never embarrass you or the fire department if made public. Dependability is your greatest asset and a quality every employer seeks. It is a quality that all people should cultivate, and it will give you a favorable reputation with all your associates.

Rule 6: *Be able to accept criticism graciously and praise, honors, and advancement modestly.* Be aware of the fact that the human personality is never completely developed, and that you have an obligation to all with whom you associate to try to improve your skills. You will be striving for promotion and advancement in the fire service. Be certain that your tactics in this competition are ethical. You can assume that your activities will be observed and evaluated by those charged with this responsibility and that your performance as seen by your supervisors will place you in some rank or order for promotion.

TODAY'S COMPANY OFFICER

A new philosophy used for the selection of fire company officers is that they must be better trained and educated as managers of firefighters, not merely the most senior firefighter available. This philosophy evolved because approximately 90 percent of a company officer's time is spent in duties other than actual emergency responses. These other duties include personnel management, training, career counseling, and administrative functions. It is essential that company officers be adequately trained to handle a wide variety of managerial duties.

The type or size of your fire department does not change the requirements that will be placed upon you as an officer. The descriptions and requirements of leadership are the same in all types of departments. From this point on in this text, we urge the reader to forget the specifics of the department and accept the obligation of company officers everywhere. The problems and solutions of leadership are universal. Effective motivational principles work in large, career departments as well as volunteer departments and are required in all parts of the world.

SUPPLEMENTAL READINGS

Fire Service Orientation and Indoctrination. 2nd ed. Stillwater, Okla.: Fire Protection Publications, Oklahoma State University, 1984.

Managing Fire Services. Washington, D.C.: International City Management Association, 1979.

Standard for Fire Officer Professional Qualifications. National Fire Protection Association, 1987.

1

Principles Of Organization

LEARNING OBJECTIVES

After completing this chapter and related *Student Guide* applications, company officer candidates should be able to:

- Distinguish between the operational organization and the administrative organization.

- Recall the principle of unity of command.

- Recognize guidelines for avoiding being sidestepped by employees.

- Explain the concept of span of control.

- State the importance of division of labor.

- Explain the concept of discipline.

- Demonstrate the ability to delegate or refer tasks and authority.

This chapter addresses NFPA 1021,
Standard for Fire Officer Professional Qualifications (1987):
2-2.4.

Chapter 1
Principles of Organization

A fire department is made up of many individuals with different backgrounds and ideas about life. The success of a fire department depends on the willingness of individuals to put aside differences and work together for the benefit of the department. It is the role of company officers to mold this group of people into a company—an effective emergency response team. Successful company officers recognize the importance of developing this cooperation and structure working relationships to achieve this goal.

All fire chiefs strive for unity within the department. To ensure that department members work together effectively, written standards are required. Examples of these documents are shown in Figure 1.1. This information is used as a tool to help guide firefighters. Fire officers must recognize that cooperation

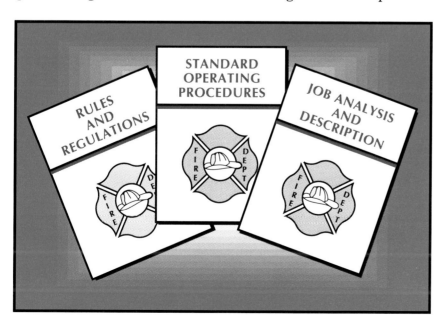

Figure 1.1 The fire department uses organizational documents like job descriptions and organizational charts to ensure cooperation between department members.

among company members is based on trust and effective communications.

Working relationships in all good departments are guided by sound management criteria. There are four basic organizational principles that company officers must use. They are:

- Unity of command
- Span of control
- Division of labor
- Discipline

UNITY OF COMMAND

Many people who study the principles of organization as a science have made the observation that a person can only report to one supervisor. If an employee is put into a position that requires reporting to more than one supervisor, a number of difficult situations can result. The most common of these situations are:

- The employee plays the supervisors against each other so none know exactly what the employee is doing, and the employee gets away with doing little or no work.

- The supervisor who yells the loudest or bangs the hardest on the desk is the one who gets the employee to do work and the other bosses get no work done.

- The employee becomes frustrated attempting to follow conflicting orders from different supervisors and gives up trying or quits the job.

- The project or task itself tends to suffer in quality because the employee may execute the task poorly trying to follow conflicting procedures.

As each situation illustrates, the violation of the one-supervisor principle leads to confusion and frustration by company members. Therefore, unity of command should be utilized to make the individual more productive and efficient. Unity of command channels direction and accountability for a company member to one company officer.

The company officer should understand that although each member of the fire department reports to one supervisor directly, indirectly everyone is still responsible to the fire chief through the chain of command. The chain of command is the pathway of responsibility from the top of the department to the bottom.

The fire chief can issue general orders that filter through the chain of command and are translated into specific work assignments for the firefighter. With unity of command, work can be broken down into specific job assignments without loss of control. An example of this is as follows:

Chief Franklin is the chief of a medium-sized fire department. He has three deputy chiefs, and each supervises three stations. Chief Franklin issues a policy that all firefighters riding in jumpseats shall wear seat belts.

Deputy Chief Smith receives the new policy and relays it to each of the station captains. Deputy Chief Smith tells Captain Jones of Station 5 of the new policy and would like him to relay it to his crew. Captain Jones understands the new policy and has a station meeting at the beginning of the next shift to inform the firefighters of the order. This is how the chain of command should work. Each firefighter is now responsible for wearing a seat belt while riding in the jumpseat of an apparatus. This policy is issued in writing and becomes part of the Standard Operating Procedures of Chief Franklin's department (Figure 1.2).

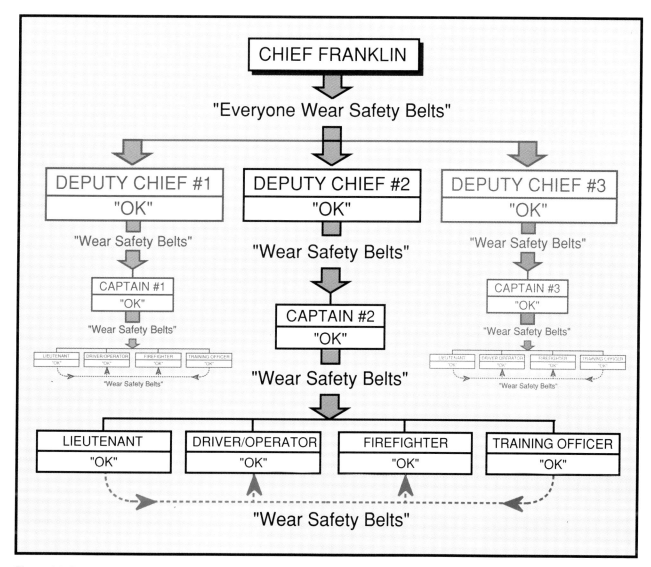

Figure 1.2 Everyone in a chain of command must receive and forward a directive to ensure successful communication.

Another important aspect of proper chain of command is that everyone receives the same communication and is aware of the message. If Chief Franklin went directly to the firefighters and announced they must wear seat belts, they would, of course, follow the chief's directive. In bypassing the deputy chiefs, captains, and so on, midmanagement personnel have been excluded from the directive. Consequently, they may not be aware of the new procedure and would be unable to ensure compliance.

Breaches In The Unity-Of-Command Concept

In reality, there are always going to be times when things do not go by the book. In emergencies, situations will arise that result in the unity of command concept being breached. The company officer must realize that there will be times the company officer's authority might be undercut or questioned by a superior or by another officer. It is important that the officer know how to deal with the problem when it occurs. To consider the options available to the company officer when such a breach occurs, consider the following example:

Paul is a probationary firefighter assigned to a fairly busy engine company. At a particular fire, Paul's captain instructed him to perform a specific task. While Paul was going to the engine to get equipment for the job, a district chief stopped him and instructed him to perform a different task. To do the second task, he would not be able to do the first task. Being a new firefighter, Paul would like to accommodate both officers. He appears to be on the spot, but it is really the officers who are on the spot. Only one task is going to get done, and one officer is going to be overruled. The possibilities are:

- Paul can do what the district chief instructs. In this case, Paul's captain will be upset because the first task assigned will not get done. His captain may even feel that the district chief has undercut his or her authority.

- Paul can do what the captain assigned. In this case, the district chief would be upset for the same reasons as the captain.

- Paul could tell the district chief about the previous assignment and let the chief decide which task has priority. At least this way Paul does not have to be responsible for the decision.

It is important for officers to realize that breaches in unity of command do occur. Therefore, fire department policies must outline procedures for handling these situations. Beyond the fact that policies must dictate how to handle such situations, officers must learn to deal with them in a positive manner. The company officer must learn to deal with breaches of command in a positive manner.

The primary point to remember when unity of command has been breached is that the problem should be examined and corrected as an organizational discrepancy rather than a personal problem.

In the case above, the two officers should meet and discuss what has happened. They should both realize that whichever task Paul completed, he was obeying the orders of a superior officer. They should let Paul know there was a breakdown of communication and that neither officer is displeased with his efforts.

There is a second type of breach in the unity of command that is probably more common than the previous situation. This breach occurs when firefighters sidestep their company officer and take problems directly to people higher in the chain of command. This situation is intolerable for several reasons (Figure 1.3). In some instances, firefighters may feel they have the upper

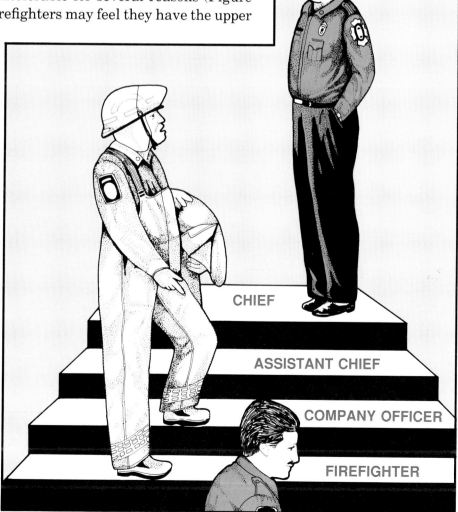

CHIEF

ASSISTANT CHIEF

COMPANY OFFICER

FIREFIGHTER

Figure 1.3 Situations in which subordinates sidestep the chain of command are intolerable.

hand by going directly to the officer's supervisor. At other times, the officer's supervisor may think that the officer is not capable of handling the firefighters' problems. In almost all situations, the sidestepping actually excludes the person who is best able to solve the problem, the company officer.

For these reasons, it is important that the company officer make the firefighter aware of the proper method of handling situations through the chain of command. In turn, the officer must know how to handle the firefighter's problems. Some guidelines that will help the officer avoid being sidestepped by the firefighter are:

- Be available to listen to the problems of the firefighter.
- Listen to problems sincerely and give them due consideration.
- Take action and let the firefighter know that something is being done (Figure 1.4).
- If the problem cannot be solved at the company level, take the concerns of the firefighter to the next level in the chain of command, AND PROVIDE NECESSARY SUPPORT.

Figure 1.4 Company officers should listen to problems and take proper action.

SPAN OF CONTROL

The span of control is the limit one person can effectively manage. In the fire service, the emergency scene is often where an officer exceeds the span of control. This is done by an officer who fails to delegate responsibilities and tries to run a "one man show." The "one man show" type of officer may destroy the potential efficiency of available emergency personnel by not devoting enough attention to the details required for making appropriate decisions. The officer becomes preoccupied with too many other activities. A serious problem with this type of action is that safety considerations are compromised for both firefighters and citizens (Figure 1.5).

Figure 1.5 Effective managers break large jobs down into smaller tasks along with assigned responsibility.

A rule of thumb for the fire service is that an officer can effectively direct or supervise five to six individuals. These individuals may be the crew of one company, or officers of other companies under the direction of the commanding officer. An example of effective span of control on the fireground is found in the incident command system where one fire officer commands one engine company, one chief officer commands one strike team of five engines, and one division supervisor (chief officer) commands five strike teams. There are several factors that affect the number of people who can be effectively supervised at any one time:

- The ability and experience of the officer
- The ability and experience of the firefighters

- The nature of the task
  - —The urgency of the task
  - —The situation under which it is performed
  - —The complexity of the task
  - —The degree of uniformity in training
  - —The occurrence rate of the task

- The relationship of tasks being performed by one individual to the tasks being performed by other individuals

- The stability and competence of the organization

These factors determine an officer's span of control. There is no standard method for determining how many firefighters can be supervised. Each situation must be examined to determine how effectively the firefighters are performing the assigned tasks and whether the officer is trying to supervise too many firefighters. When an officer feels that the span of control has been exceeded, that officer must delegate authority to other people. Remember: INEFFECTIVE DELEGATORS MUST DIRECTLY SUPERVISE ALL UNDER THEIR COMMAND.

The decision to delegate authority to complete a task is often difficult. The difficulty may be that the officer feels an obligation or commitment to guarantee that every task is done. There may be a doubt in the officer's mind that the delegated task will be completed in a manner that will meet the standards of the department. Feelings like these are natural and show that the officer is genuinely interested in doing a good job.

When delegating a task, the officer must exercise some discretion to ensure that the assigned firefighter is capable of doing the job. The officer should attempt to pick the right firefighter for the right job, being careful that the job is not beyond the ability of the individual chosen.

Keep in mind that delegation of an assignment must be accompanied with appropriate authority, and trust that the individual will achieve the desired results using proper methods. It is difficult for anyone to accomplish a task without being given the necessary authority to complete the assignment.

Another important consideration in the delegation of authority is to make the objective clear to the firefighter. This goes beyond describing the task itself. The officer should describe the task and clarify its relationship to the overall goal or objective. In addition, the officer must make clear what resources are available and what time and safety constraints apply to the assignment.

Most administrators recognize that the span of control is a real limitation and expect authority to be delegated. It is also realized that those accepting delegated authority will make mistakes. As a general rule, when authority is delegated and accepted earnestly, mistakes made by the firefighters should be considered as subjects for training rather than as subjects for discipline.

DIVISION OF LABOR

An effective managerial concept is to break large jobs down into smaller tasks. These tasks are then assigned to specific individuals (Figure 1.6).

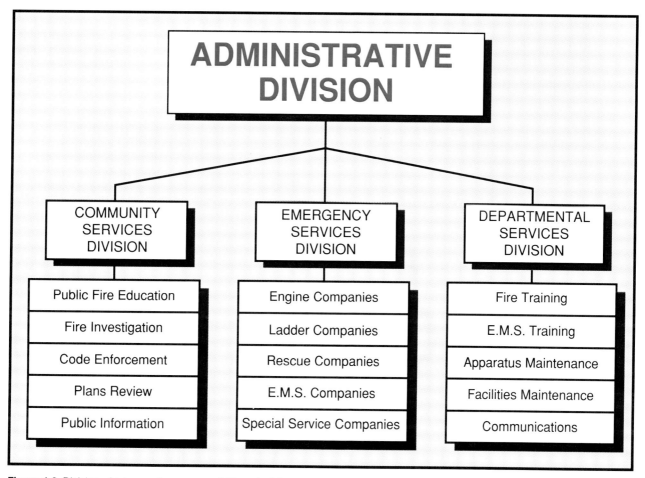

Figure 1.6 Division of labor assigns responsibility to individuals. Without the division of labor, each officer would blame another every time something went wrong.

The division of labor concept is necessary in the fire service for several reasons: to assign responsibility; to prevent duplication of effort; and to make specific, clear-cut assignments.

To accomplish the work assignments within a fire department, the assignments are divided into groupings. These groupings include the type of task, geographical area, and time. Common divisions in a fire department include emergency services, community services, and departmental services. Within each grouping, subgroups are assigned to meet the requirements of the more specific tasks assigned to the group. A good example is the arrangement of engine and truck companies in the emergency services division. Each company is responsible for performing certain tasks that help meet the general objectives of the shift commander and the department (Figure 1.7).

Another consideration in division of labor is the number of people needed to accomplish these tasks. Fire departments typically assign teams of firefighters to each company. Each team is responsible for performing the duties assigned to that company.

For the division of labor principle to be effective, all positions within the organization must be clearly outlined. This can be accomplished by analyzing each position and identifying all the skills and knowledge necessary for the job. Job analysis and job descriptions are critical to assist personnel in performing their many tasks. All personnel must know what their specific responsibilities are and understand what is expected of them.

Specialization is an important principle of the division of labor. Tasks cannot simply be assigned at random, as few people are capable of doing all things well. When making job assignments, consideration must be given to using the best person available for the job. Another way of determining personnel work assignments is to train individuals to perform particular jobs.

Special training and specific jobs are used extensively in the fire service. Fire departments commonly place emergency work

Figure 1.7 Administrators and department members alike must be committed to meeting organizational goals.

tasks into similar groups and assign personnel and equipment to handle these tasks. This is done by forming special units such as engine, truck, and rescue companies. Not only are several types of fire companies used for specific purposes, but personnel within a particular company may be trained for specific tasks. Hazardous materials teams are now common in many fire departments and are an example of this task orientation.

Care must be taken to provide adequate cross training so the various companies are able to perform other tasks with proficiency. One of the advantages of cross training is that it enables different fire companies to work together well because each company officer understands the capabilities, requirements, and needs of the other.

DISCIPLINE

Traditionally, discipline has been understood to mean correction or punishment as covered in Chapter 9. In this chapter, discipline refers to an organization's responsibility to provide the direction needed to satisfy the goals and objectives it has identified. In other words, discipline means setting the limits or boundaries for expected performance and enforcing them.

A fire department organization must share its mission statement and objectives with all of its members. This will enable all firefighters to know what is expected of them and what must be done to work toward achieving the goals of the department. Discipline may be defined as a teaching method used to enforce the organizational limits.

Direction may come in the form of rules, regulations, policies and procedures, and standard operating procedures. Regardless of the name used, however, rules must define how the department plans to operate. Furthermore, these rules must be clearly written and presented. This does not mean that giving each member a copy of the rules or placing them in each station satisfies the department's obligation to provide direction. The fire department must make a concerted effort to disseminate the information contained in the rules and regulations. Periodic formal training on this subject is critical.

Department officers must also show their commitment to the goals of the fire department by being fair and honest in the application of rules as well as abiding by the rules themselves. If the administrators are not committed to meeting the organizational goals, they cannot expect commitment from the department members. Fire officers must lead by example and model the intent of the organizational goals in order to maintain the proper direction at the company level.

SUMMARY

Without a valid organizational base, fire departments will not be able to attain their goals effectively and efficiently. There are several principles of organization. These are unity of command, span of control, division of labor, and discipline. These principles are not only important on the fireground, but must also be used in the daily routine. For the company officer to be an effective leader, he or she must know how and be willing to use these principles in both emergency and nonemergency situations.

SUPPLEMENTAL READINGS

Effective Supervisory Practices. 2nd ed. Washington D.C.: International City Management Association, 1984.

Gratz, David B. *Fire Department Management: Scope and Method.* Beverly Hills: Glencoe Press, 1972.

Management in the Fire Service. Didactic Systems, Inc. Boston: National Fire Protection Association, 1977.

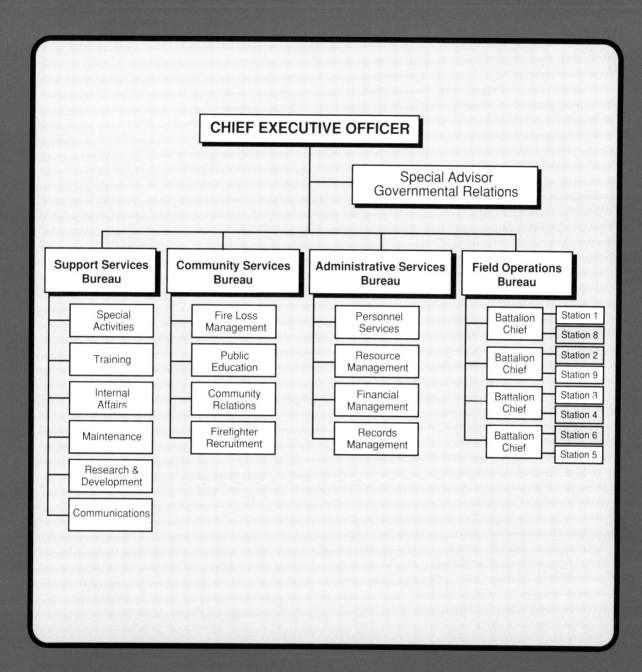

Organizational Structure

LEARNING OBJECTIVES

After completing this chapter and related *Student Guide* applications, company officer candidates should be able to:

- Explain why large organizations are composed of smaller, component organizations.
- Explain the scalar structure of fire department organization.
- Recognize the relationships that exist between line and staff personnel.
- Distinguish between centralized and decentralized authority.
- Identify basic company organizational structures.

This chapter addresses NFPA 1021,
Standard for Fire Officer Professional Qualifications (1987):
2-5.3
2-5.4.

Chapter 2
Organizational Structure

Everyone has experience with a variety of organizational structures. From little league ball teams to family groups, we participate in structured activities on a daily basis. The fire service has many unique characteristics concerning organization. It requires a distinct team spirit, a high degree of leadership from its officers, and a need for a strong disciplinary influence. Emergency service personnel must also be capable of instant reaction on the fireground.

THE SCALAR STRUCTURE AS A BASE OF FIRE DEPARTMENT ORGANIZATION

The term used to describe the common organizational structure in the fire service is "scalar." Scalar is defined as "having an uninterrupted series of steps" or a "chain of authority."

The scalar organization is a paramilitary, pyramid type of organization with authority centralized at the top (Figure 2.1).

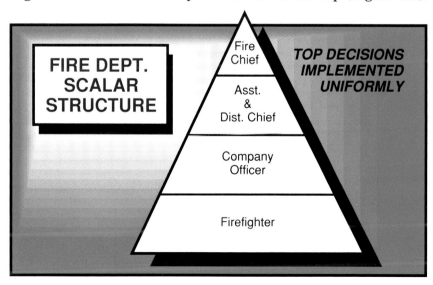

Figure 2.1 Most fire departments operate in a scalar structure. This allows decisions to be made at the top of the structure and implemented uniformly throughout the organization.

Decisions are directed down from the top of the structure through intermediate levels to the base. Information in turn is transmitted up from the bottom through the structure to the positions at the top.

Fire departments are scalar organizations. The companies are organized in the scalar manner, the companies fit into a scalar battalion, and so on. A typical fire department organizational chart appears in Figure 2.2.

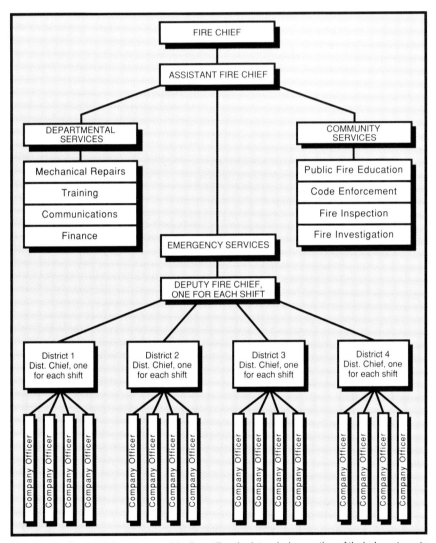

Figure 2.2 Fire administrators graphically outline the intended operation of their departments by using organizational charts. A typical organizational chart is shown here.

For years, many fire service individuals perceived fire departments as strictly scalar organizations. With close evaluation, it became clear, however, that operations did not always follow the rigid scalar form. In the pure form of the scalar principle of management, there is an unbroken chain, or *SCALE,* of supervisors from the top to the bottom of the organization. This chain describes the flow of authority. Any action or reaction taking place in the group must pass through this well-defined path.

To follow the true scalar form would be to pattern after the basic organizational structure of the first organized fire fighting force. This "original" group established in Rome by Caesar Augustus around 6 B.C. followed the military form of that time and was structured into battalions answering directly to the Emperor.

There are a number of modern fire chiefs that consider their station in life to be similar to an Emperor. The fact is that quicker action is accomplished in many cases by direct communications at a lower level. There must be one central point in the organization which exercises overall directional control of all the parts. Modern managers of human resources allow for some decentralization. This means that certain decisions are delegated to lower levels and cross communications should occur.

The true scalar structure is well suited for dealing with emergency situations for several reasons:

- The span of control is kept manageable.
- Information is centralized for decision making.
- A functional chain of command is maintained.

LINE AND STAFF

Line and staff are terms that refer to a concept of traditional origin. This concept separates a fire department into two distinct sections: line, those who fight fire; and staff, those who support the emergency operations. The evolution of this concept has been detailed as follows:

During the 19th century, fire departments existed primarily to fight fire. Secondary objectives—fire prevention, training, and administration—often required special skills beyond those normally needed by firefighters. Personnel with special skills were retained by fire departments to support the firefighter, and were termed staff. It was basically summed up by an old battalion chief who stated, "If you ride a truck, you are line, but if you service the truck, you are staff."

Through the first half of the 20th century, the original fire service goal of primarily fighting fire began to change. Meeting this goal meant having the most efficient fire fighting units, yet in spite of the high degree of efficiency, fire losses continued to rise from year to year. It became questionable whether fighting fire alone was the most effective method for controlling fire loss.

The modification of the goal of fire departments has not ended in a shift away from efficient fire fighting, but now includes other methods of controlling fire loss. Fire departments now agree that the goal of the fire service is "the protection of life and property."

To achieve this goal, many departments are freeing firefighters for fire suppression activities by placing civilians in non-fire fighting positions such as inspection, public education, and fire alarm dispatching.

With this shift, the definition between line and staff has become less distinct. Line, which always implied the meeting of the primary goal of the fire service through fire suppression, might now be applied to other non-fire fighting positions. A fire prevention inspector who was always a staff member of the fire department can be considered a line member under the new perspective.

In most jurisdictions, the traditional understanding has remained. A shift in the traditional line of authority has begun, however, to include direct involvement of staff personnel. Line of authority refers to the use of authority from the top of an organization to its members, known as chain of command.

It is important that each member of the department understand that a prescribed sequence of authority exists. Each person must realize the importance of the chain of command and recognize his or her position in the chain. The company officer must realize that the goals of the fire service are expanding and that to meet these new demands, the chain of command is becoming more elastic. This means that fire fighting companies may be placed in a position of overlapping authority.

Traditional Staff Advisory

In the traditional view of fire department goals, a staff advisory system exists (Figure 2.3). The information flow through this system depends upon the department's view of the service it plans to provide. The traditional staff advisory structure has the staff personnel in a separate division providing advice to top management. This has proven to be an effective method for making decisions and implementing them through the fire suppression chain of command.

Staff Direct Implementation Method

The current method of using staff personnel is to route their advice through upper and middle department management. The technical data provided by staff positions is then put into directives and sent directly through the chain of command. This method works well for policy matters. However, because of the bulk of information that must go down through the chain of command, it is not well suited for procedural matters.

To avoid bogging down the system, an alternative method for disseminating management decisions can be used. Instead of upper management implementing the decision through the line chain of command, implementation can be delegated to the staff division (Figure 2.4). The staff positions can then deal directly with the line structure to implement the decision. In these instances, an authority overlap occurs.

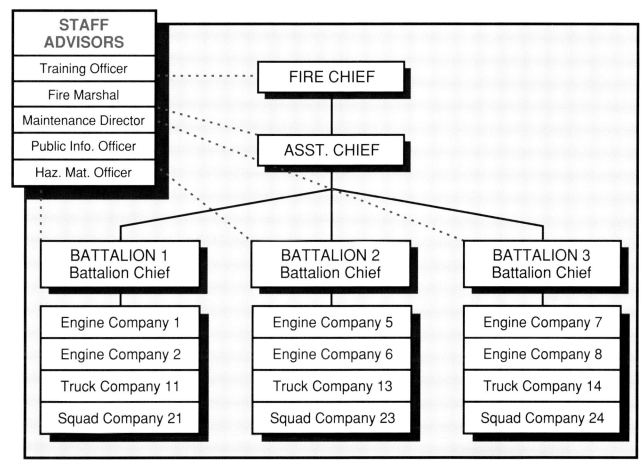

Figure 2.3 The traditional staff advisory structure is an effective method of making and implementing decisions.

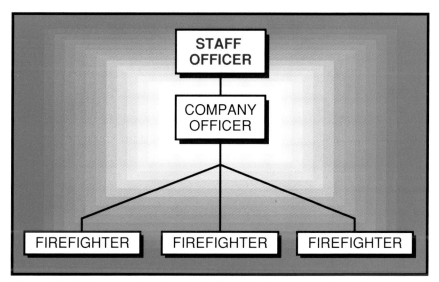

Figure 2.4 Staff personnel can be used to directly implement procedures through untraditional methods.

With this overlap, unity of command is partially altered. A line member is dealing with an intermediate staff advisor. The overlap can result in either chaos or increased efficiency.

The result is more dependent on the attitudes of those involved than on any other factor. For this reason it is important that the company officer understand and accept the situation. The company officer must recognize the benefits of working with overlapping authority.

There are four basic structures or methods of overlapping authority:

- Undesirable overlap
- Staff direct advice
- Mutual staff/line overlap
- Line advice to staff

Undesirable Overlap

The least effective overlap situation is to have the staff position deal with the firefighter independent of the company officer. The firefighter must not be put in the position of being caught between two bosses (Figure 2.5). Both the firefighter's performance and morale are likely to suffer.

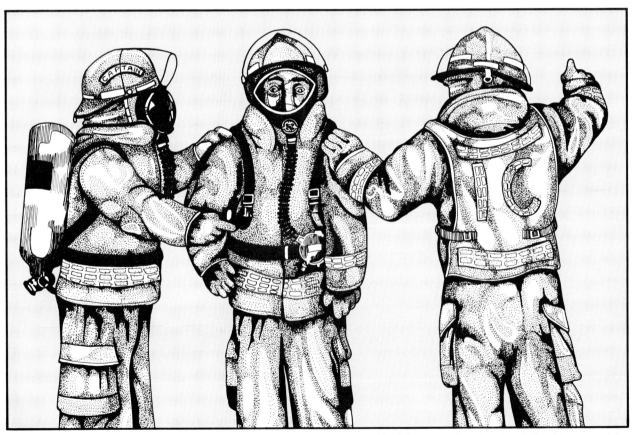

Figure 2.5 To put the firefighter into a position of having two bosses is not acceptable. Other ways of overlapping staff and line supervision should be used.

Staff Direct Advice

The overlap can be in the form of a staff position directly advising the company officer. This situation is commonly used to introduce new equipment or procedures (Figure 2.6). The company officer is given training directly by the staff position and then the officer trains the company. The staff position keeps the authority to correct the implementation because the authority to incorporate the change has been decentralized to the staff position.

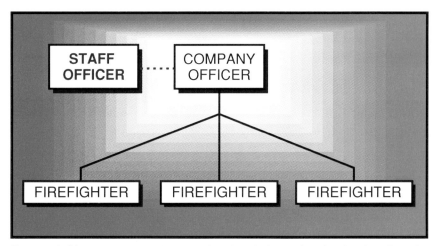

Figure 2.6 Often when new equipment is introduced, the overlap situation that allows the staff position to directly advise the company officer is used.

Mutual Staff/Line Overlap

Another method of overlap is for the staff position to work with the line position to implement a change (Figure 2.7). The line position and staff position have equal input into explaining the task to the firefighter. Pilot programs often use this method. For example, a staff position works with the company officer to find the most effective method of using a new piece of equipment

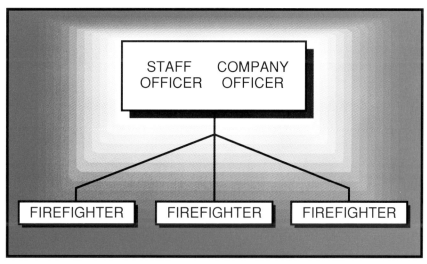

Figure 2.7 The company officer can work closely with the staff person to mutually implement procedures.

or concept. The company officer gives knowledge of the company's capabilities, the staff position gives knowledge of the new method.

Line Advice To Staff

Another method is for the line position to give command of the company to the staff position. The line officer provides information or advice to the staff officer, who then incorporates the line officer's advice into the implementation (Figure 2.8). Personnel evaluations and promotions are often handled in this manner. This is almost a direct reversal of the staff direct advice method.

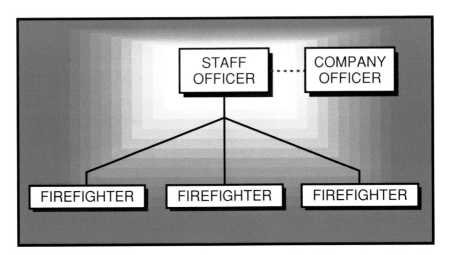

Figure 2.8 In some instances, the line officer may assume the advisory role and allow the staff personnel to control the company.

AUTHORITY TO IMPLEMENT

Authority refers to the legal ability of an individual to make and implement decisions for which the individual is held accountable. There are two types of authority: centralized and decentralized.

The difference between centralized authority and decentralized authority is the level at which decisions are made. In a centralized authority structure, decisions are made by one person at the top of the structure. Decentralized authority allows the decisions to be made at a lower level, with the effects of the decisions reported through the structure.

Regardless of the level at which decision-making authority is placed, accountability for the decisions is almost always centralized. As a general rule, no one in a fire department has absolute authority to avoid accounting to a higher authority (even the chief is accountable to the local governing body).

Decentralized authority is basically delegation of authority. This delegation is the same as discussed in the previous chapter except that it is on a departmental level. The chief delegates authority to make decisions and implement plans to officers, but is still accountable for any decisions made.

The decentralizing process varies. Decentralization is not a blank check for total authority; rather, it means that authority is granted to accomplish specific tasks at different levels. The fire chief might give the authority to make policy changes to an assistant chief while granting authority to service equipment to the company level (Figure 2.9). The chief may also decentralize the authority to make certain decisions only in specific areas. An example of this occurs when a chief delegates to the company officer the authority to decide what duty uniform will be worn during a shift but keeps authority to determine what hair length is acceptable.

Decentralization of authority is advantageous for handling day-to-day matters. Most business can be handled at lower levels in an organization, allowing upper management personnel to concentrate on more important matters. The details resulting from a decision do not have to be reported, but the effects of the decision do. For example, the chief does not need to know specifically that the maintenance department is going to replace two pistons and six valves on Engine 23. The chief does need to know that the decision to overhaul Engine 23 has been made.

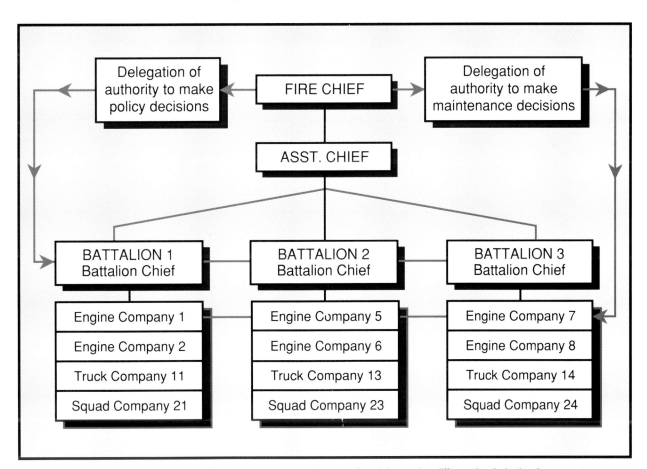

Figure 2.9 The authority to perform certain tasks or make decisions is often delegated to different levels in the department.

As much as possible, decision making authority should be delegated to the level where decisions are likely to be made. However, with decentralization of authority, the possibility of a duplication of efforts exists. To avoid this, department policies must define what decisions can be made and under what conditions. A review system must also be established to study the effects of decentralized decisions and to ensure accountability.

COMPANY ORGANIZATIONAL STRUCTURES

The company officer needs to study different organizational structures and under what conditions each works best. Additionally, the officer must examine how the company organization fits into the department and what structural forms it takes. It is unrealistic to adopt one approach and expect it to meet all situations. The members must be aware that the organizational structure is elastic, changing when necessary to meet immediate needs and then returning to the normally used organizational design.

The Social Structure

Fire companies include individuals from different walks of life with a variety of attitudes, opinions, and backgrounds. These individuals enter this organizational structure called a fire company with many expectations. They also expect a number of returns from the group and anticipate making certain contributions to the organizational structure. When a firefighter joins a company, specific kinds of behavior are expected. It is also anticipated that certain rewards will be granted for appropriate behavior. By the same token, it also follows that inappropriate or unacceptable behavior could be punished by disciplinary action or rejection of the individual by the remainder of the group. Both socially and operationally the individual and the organization, represented by the other members of the company, have mutual expectations about each other.

Initially, individuals who join a fire company go through a process of adjustment. It will take some time to learn more about what constitutes acceptable behavior and what types of results are expected and rewarded. During this period of adjustment, new members of the organization will be learning their roles and what is expected of them by the other members of the company and the formal leader. Just as every individual in a fire company, the company itself has a personality based on the social structure and values, needs, and objectives of the individuals comprising that company. Both fire companies and individuals have personalities. The company's personality will also have an impact on the goals, objectives, and the attitudes projected from the administrative levels of the fire department structure. It is the positive personality aspects contributed by these individuals in conjuction with the positive attributes projected by the company that are the major factors in the success of the fire department organization.

Flat Centralized Organizational Structure

The flat organizational structure is the simplest. It consists of one person with all the authority supervising the group on a one-to-one basis (Figure 2.10). The interaction between individuals is minimal and information flow among individual members is small.

The flat organization is well suited to accomplish tasks when none of the tasks are interdependent. The division of station duties is a good example of the use of a flat structure in that the central authority makes the decision in each situation. The major limitation of the flat structure is the span of control of the person having authority. The result of this limitation is that the flat organization has trouble dealing with complex tasks. An example of this would be extrication of several injured victims from an overturned automobile.

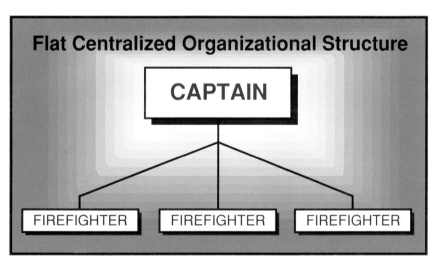

Figure 2.10 The simplest form of organization, a flat structure, involves the officer dealing with the firefighters on a one-to-one basis.

The Scalar Organizational Structure

The scalar organizational structure is a second type of centralized authority. As previously defined in this chapter, it is an organization having an uninterrupted series of steps with authority centralized at the top.

The limitation of the scalar structure is its rigid format. Although scalar structure works well on the fireground, it tends to bog down in routine work. During everyday operations, the information movement between levels can be slow. Other disadvantages are the following:

- Individual initiative is hampered because of separation between the field members and decision-making levels.

- Movement of information through intermediate levels tends to distort information or change the context because of misunderstandings and personalities of intermediate level persons.

- Scalar structures tend to promote static organizations.

Officers can reduce the effect of these disadvantages by using a less centralized structure when a rigid framework is not required.

The Circular Organizational Structure

The third structure of centralized authority is the circular structure. The circular structure involves a central authority interacting with the individuals of a group, and members interacting among themselves (Figure 2.11). The circular structure is excellent for problem solving because of the high level of interaction. The result is that fresh and innovative solutions are found. The personal commitment of members in circular structures tends to be higher because of the ability to receive feedback and provide input.

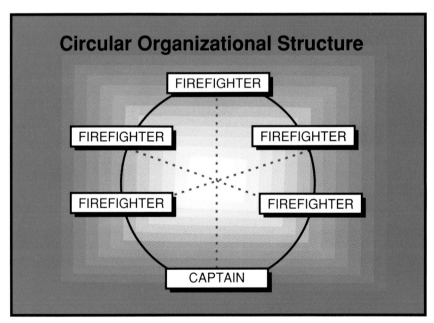

Figure 2.11 A circular structure is an excellent problem solver.

The limitation of the circular structure is that it is slow for implementing tasks. The time lag occurs as a result of the input/feedback process. Emergency situations simply do not allow time for involved discussion before a decision is made. The circular structure can be used effectively for problem solving, but can be cumbersome as a task-implementer.

The major disadvantages of the circular structure are:

- The group may provide input to the point that minor details receive too much attention. When details become important items of contention, personalities dominate the input.

- Circular structures can break up the group. Members may take sides over an issue. This can be especially critical if the officer fails to manage the group.

SUMMARY

The fire service of today is a dynamic force organized around a scalar framework. The range of demands placed upon the fire service by modern technology requires the structure to be flexible. The company officer must recognize this flexibility, and he or she must adapt to the demands placed upon the company.

The company officer should try to recognize possible uses of the basic structures within the company structure. The company officer should make an effort to see which method produces the best results under different situations and then modify personnel assignments to make the company more effective.

The objective of the fire service is expanding. To meet this objective, staff personnel are more directly involved with the fire company. Companies may find themselves involved in inspections, public education, and training in close relationship with staff personnel. Company officers have the opportunity to harness individual potential to meet the expanding objectives of the fire service.

In many fire departments, the concept of line and staff positions have appeared to establish status problems. Line members are viewed as important, first-class members because they are directly responsible for fire control, emergency medical activities, rescue activities, and other direct situations that effect the outcome of emergencies. On the other hand, staff members are often seen as second-class members of the group because of their support status. In many instances, staff members object vigorously to the implication that they are not as important as fire companies, rescue squad members, and other line officials. The fact is that a person's worth to an organization is measured in terms of the net contribution to the meeting of the organization's overall goals and objectives. Therefore, it is critical that all members of the fire department, both line and staff, focus on meeting these goals and objectives together. It is this joint effort that makes companies strong, efficient, and effective.

SUPPLEMENTAL READINGS

Effective Supervisory Practices. 2nd ed. Washington D.C.: International City Management Association, 1984.

Fire Protection Handbook. 15th ed. Quincy: National Fire Protection Association, 1981.

Fire Service Orientation and Indoctrination. 2nd ed. Stillwater, Okla.: Fire Protection Publications, Oklahoma State University, 1984.

Gratz, David B. *Fire Department Management: Scope and Method.* Beverly Hills: Glencoe Press, 1972.

Hicks, Herbert G., and C. Ray Gullett. *Management.* 4th ed. New York: McGraw-Hill, 1981.

Leadership In The Fire Service. 1st ed. Stillwater, Okla.: Fire Protection Publications, Oklahoma State University, 1967.

Management in the Fire Service. Didactic Systems, Inc. Boston: National Fire Protection Association, 1977.

3

Communications

LEARNING OBJECTIVES

After completing this chapter and related *Student Guide* applications, company officer candidates should be able to:

- Recognize the essential elements of effective communications.

- Recall ways in which people communicate.

- Recognize barriers to effective communication.

- Distinguish between hearing and listening.

- Distinguish between orders and directives.

- Recall types of information likely to be communicated via the "grapevine."

- State the importance of effective fireground communications.

- Recall hinderances to effective fireground communications.

- Demonstrate the ability to
  —Communicate effectively orally.
  —Communicate effectively in writing.

This chapter addresses NFPA 1021,
Standard for Fire Officer Professional Qualifications (1987):

2-2.3	3-3	4-12.1
2-2.4	3-6.3	4-1.3
2-2.5	3-6.4	
2-3.2	3-6.5	
2-14.1	3-6.6	
2-14.2	3-6.7	
2-14.3		
2-14.4		

Chapter 3
Communications

The concept of communications is vague to most people; although, it is a lifetime activity starting at birth. When asked to define communications, a typical response might be, "talking between two people" or "words," or some other simplistic answer. These answers are only partially correct. They fail to identify communication as a process that exchanges ideas and information between two parties.

The communication process exists in many forms, but all communication accomplishes the task of exchanging information. Regardless of the form used, the communication process is comprised of five essential elements:

- A person to send the information—the "sender"
- The actual message
- A method for the information to be transmitted
- A person to receive the information—the "receiver"
- Feedback from the receiver to the sender that the information was received and understood

COMMUNICATIONS AS A PROCESS
The Sender And Receiver

Communication begins with the sender or message initiator (Figure 3.1 on next page). The process begins when the sender perceives that another person must perform in a given manner to help meet the needs of the sender. The sender must convey to the second person (receiver) the intended message of the sender. The sender must develop a message and method of transmission that the receiver can understand.

Communication is a process involving much more than just a message and its sender. Communication is aimed at creating understanding between the sender and the receiver. Each person in a conversation acts as both a sender and receiver (Figure 3.2). The sender must be aware that the receiver may perceive the situation being discussed differently because of their differing backgrounds. We all use our background and past experiences to interpret what we see and hear. Not only do we see things differently, but two people rarely interpret a statement they have heard in exactly the same way. Difference in perception of a situation is often a barrier to communication. This means that the sender must consider the feelings and personal background of the receiver. The sender must develop thoughts into an understandable package. This package is called the message. The message is the thought that is transmitted. The method of transmission is called the medium.

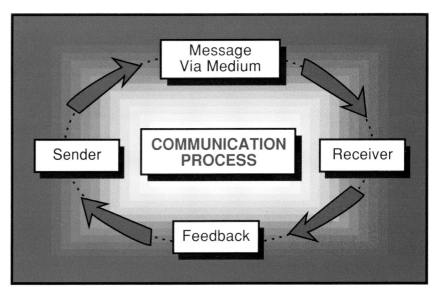

Figure 3.1 Communication involves a process of two or more people sending and receiving information. This process requires that the people understand each other.

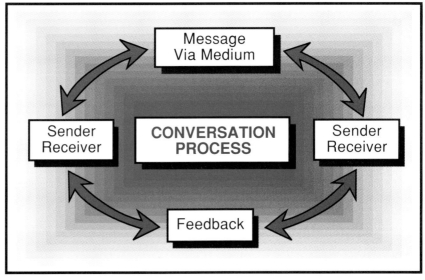

Figure 3.2 Because each person in a conversation acts as a sender and a receiver, communications can be described as a dual process.

THE MESSAGE

The message communicated between parties must convey the intended meaning and be in a form that is understood. This process is sometimes harder than it may appear. The objective of the sender is to develop a message that conveys what is wanted or expected. It serves no purpose to send or request information that is neither needed nor wanted. Useless information only clutters or confuses the communication process.

The receiver must be able to clearly understand what is expected or is being asked. If this essential task is not accomplished, the entire communication process begins to falter. Consider the following example:

A plumber writes to a government agency requesting advice on using hydrochloric acid for cleaning pipe.

Answer: "The efficiency of this solution is indisputable but the corrosive residue is incompatible with metallic permanence."

Plumber: "What?"

Translation: "Don't use hydrochloric acid; it eats the heck out of the pipe."

In the development of effective messages, the sender must be aware of the ways in which messages may be interpreted or misinterpreted. Careful selection of words, phraseology, tone, and the manner in which messages are sent are other key considerations. Other barriers that may prevent a message from being understood or misinterpreted are the following:

- Time of day
- Level of activity
- Education levels of both parties
- Personal background and experience
- Personality
- Relationship of the sender and the receiver
- Language or terminology

As was previously discussed, the sender and the receiver roles are exchanged during the communication process. The company officer must understand that both roles exist and be able to communicate effectively from either position.

THE MEDIUM

The medium of communication is simply the channel by which the message is delivered between two parties.

The selection of a communication channel will depend upon many factors such as available time, purpose, language, or the information being delivered. For example, it may be acceptable to verbally communicate a message on the fireground rather than trying to send a written message. One method is appropriate for the situation; the other may deliver the message, but not in a timely fashion. Other examples of communication channels, in addition to spoken words or written messages, are physical actions of an individual, visual displays for training, or the use of various tones and sounds. Each may appropriately convey the message in the most effective way possible. The end result should be an understanding of the message by the receiver.

Company officers primarily use the spoken word as the channel for communicating with other firefighters and the public. The main form of verbal exchange is either face-to-face or via portable radios. Because of the directness of these channels of communication, officers should use language that is easily understood by firefighters.

The officer must always consider the possibility of a language barrier or misinterpretation of terminology. The best way to keep this from happening is to use simple, direct words in a brief, uncomplicated message. This is particularly important during emergency situations when excitement and activity levels are high. The channel of communication and the design of the message are key considerations that the company officer must learn to address when communicating with others.

The scope of medium in the communication process includes the nonverbal communication commonly called "body language." When we communicate orally, the receiver often "hears" what we don't say louder than our words. Our gestures, facial expressions, stance, and even how we dress sometimes speak louder than our voice. What is communicated nonverbally may not be what we had in mind, but it is usually a large part of how the message is interpreted.

Another important medium used for communicating information is through written words, graphic displays, or the use of commonly accepted symbols. In this form of communication, the receiver must visually identify the message, interpret the meaning, and respond or provide feedback that the message was understood. Examples of written forms of communication are as follows:

- Letters or other correspondence
- Standard Operating Procedures (SOPs)
- Symbols used in pre-incident planning
- Training aids (graphics, charts, and photos)

Each example of written communication must convey the information that the sender wants the receiver to understand and must be in a form that is appropriate for the message.

LISTENING

As supervisors, fire officers spend most of their time communicating, but communicating includes listening. The topic discussed here is not how to get others to listen to us, but how to listen *ourselves*. Listening to others takes up a good part of our time every day. Research has shown, however, that the average person takes in only a fraction of what is heard. Fortunately, listening can be learned. Good listening skills pay off in greater efficiency and personal satisfaction (Figure 3.3). First, you must realize that listening is an active process.

Some people merely *hear;* they do not listen. Understanding a message requires that an active role in listening exist. Alert facial expressions and posture are examples of a good listener. Questions and comments from the listener show interest and encourage the speaker to expand on what is being said. These actions let the speaker know the message is being received.

Understanding the speaker's words is as important as hearing their sounds. Words have different meanings for different people, so the listener must work to understand the speaker's

Figure 3.3 Listening is an active process which requires a person to be alert and interested.

intent. Listening with understanding involves interpreting word meanings, that is, listening with understanding involves empathy. Empathy is the ability to put oneself in another's place, and it is an essential skill for the fire officer.

Empathy means that the supervisor understands the employee's feelings and motives. A good supervisor will set aside time every day if necessary so employees can talk in private.

Bias or prejudice can be a barrier to communication. We may not like someone because of their age, sex, race, or religion, so we listen without really hearing. The company officer should give everyone a chance to be heard.

Boredom can make us hear without really listening. If the subject does not interest us or if the speaker is dull, we drift into other thoughts. This is a waste of the speaker's time and effort as well as our own. Another example of nonlistening is *pretending* to listen. You may fool the speaker by responding to what is being said with nods of agreement, but you cannot fool yourself.

A good environment for listening is important. Absence of loud background noise, a comfortable temperature, and the expectation of both sender and receiver that the message will be important enough to merit attention make for a good listening environment. The company officer must constantly be aware of the listening environment or run the risk of both not being heard and not hearing others.

Listening is an important tool for company officers in dealing with their subordinates. One of the highest compliments a firefighter can pay the supervisor is "I can talk to the captain. The captain listens."

FORMAL COMMUNICATIONS
Written Policies And Procedures
Policies and procedures are examples of "standing" or "repeat-use" plans designed to deal with the recurring problems of an organization. Communicating these plans in writing helps ensure that organizational objectives will be met throughout all divisions of the department.

A policy is a guide to decision making within an organization. Policies originate with top management in the fire department and disseminate the decisions that fire officers or other management personnel make. Not only does a policy aid in decision making, it also defines the boundaries within which administration expects the fire officer to act.

Some policies arise from appeal to management for guidance in making decisions about exceptional cases. For instance, a fire officer who does not know how a certain case should be handled might refer the matter to a superior. Appeal is made upward until someone in the hierarchy is reached who has proper authority to make the decision. At the same time, the decision maker may write a policy for handling similar cases, or may simply use the decision as a precedent to act as department policy.

Sometimes unwritten policies originate from the way in which managers perceive standard operating policies in the organization. Such policies are implied in the routine activities of the organization. Implied policies often develop where no clear policy exists. This is especially true in fire departments where policies are not written, or if written policies are extremely out of date. The informal policies followed generally come from the traditional way things have been done.

Unwritten policies can come to have as much force as if they were written. Employee organizations may also desire to use unwritten "past practice" as a tool to mold written standards or to establish a precedent for settling grievances. It can be seen how deeply rooted tradition is when a department tries to change from traditional implied policies to newer written ones.

Policy is often imposed upon fire departments by federal, state, and local government. Equal opportunity employment practices are imposed by the federal government and the Fair Labor Standards Act. Many state governments are now adopting federal standards for the control of hazardous materials. Local code ordinances have an impact on fire department operations.

Policies must be put in writing to make management's intent clear. Written policies give department members a reference point for decision making. They form the department policy manual. Written policies make for more uniform, consistent practices throughout the organization.

The company officer's duty in regard to policies is to understand and discreetly apply them on the job. Correct interpretation of department policy may require consultation (through proper chain of command) with higher management. Often, instruction for fire officers in department policies and their interpretation is necessary. Company officers must also teach policies to subordinates and new employees as part of their indoctrination.

A procedure is a formal communication closely related to policies. While a policy is a guide for thinking or decision making, a procedure is a detailed guide for action.

A procedure details in writing the steps to be followed in carrying out organizational policy for some specific, recurring problem or situation. For instance, most organizations with personnel departments require persons seeking employment to first apply at the personnel office. This procedure for processing new applicants then directs the personnel department (and they, in turn, direct the applicant) through the successive steps that must be followed in the application process.

STANDARD OPERATING PROCEDURES

Progressive fire departments provide their personnel with specific, detailed information. Development and use of the SOP (standard operating procedure) format allows an organization to make the best use of human resources. Having the basic point of reference helps all members of the organization perform to a measurable standard. Misunderstandings about techniques, responsibilities, and procedures are reduced by having the specific SOP on a subject to reference. Emergency response and operating at incidents require clear, decisive action on the part of incident commanders, company officers, and firefighters. Standard operating procedures provide the methods by which specific action is taken. They are the basis of all skills training and are the building blocks with which the entire organization is constructed.

Orders And Directives

Orders are directives based upon the authority delegated to the officer to direct the administration of a policy, procedure, or method. However, directives are not orders.

When a company officer directs a firefighter to polish his or her shoes according to department policy, it is an order. Written orders may be issued as bulletins from top management or from chief officer to company officer. The company officer may issue orders involving the operation of the station, for example, by writing them on a chalkboard or posting them on a bulletin board. Formal communication of an order in writing is often used to follow up a verbal order. This repetition of an order assures understanding.

Directives are not based upon the administrative policy, procedure, or method, but are essential to implementing these formal guidelines. A company officer telling Jones to help wash the truck has given Jones a directive. Jones understands he must wash the truck because of the officer's authority to supervise the company. The officer and Jones realize that Jones was not given an order. Should Jones fail to comply it would lead to disciplinary action because of insubordination, not for failing to comply with any departmental policy of washing the truck. However, if Jones were ordered to get a haircut and did not, Jones would be subject to discipline for breach of a departmental policy in addition to insubordination.

The officer must learn to recognize when to issue orders and when to issue directives. When the officer is issuing directives, more tact and skill should be employed than when issuing orders. There is no doubt that the officer has the authority to direct the company, but it is a poor practice to rely solely on this authority to motivate firefighters. Often, the best test of authority is that it does not need to be tested. Orders, however, do not grant the officer much freedom to tactfully motivate, because the authority is legally based on policy that an officer cannot control. From this basis it becomes clear that directing, when possible, is in some respects better than ordering.

Fireground Orders

On the fireground there is the ever-present danger of injury or death. This danger places extreme pressure on fireground officers, and alters the perspective of orders and directives. On the fireground, the officer issues many instructions, directives, and requests. However, because of the seriousness of the situation, all of these communications are generally considered orders. To avoid confusion, some departments choose to differentiate between regular orders and fireground orders.

Giving orders on the fireground is an important supervisory duty for the fire officer. If an order is understood and carried out, the work gets done. Besides getting things accomplished, orders aid in training and developing cooperation. Properly given orders result in the need for less supervision in the future as employees learn what is expected of them.

A command officer may be understandably apprehensive about giving orders on the fireground. Nonetheless, it is important that the officer control anxiety, uneasiness, or excitement while giving orders. Orders must be issued calmly and must be clear, concise, and complete.

FIREGROUND COMMUNICATIONS

The company officer, whether or not he or she becomes the incident commander, has an implied duty to initiate, maintain, and control a vital network of communications. This network must be the basis of providing essential information to the various officers involved with the fireground operations. The quality of information is more important than the quantity of information.

But the information must be complete and accurately convey the message intended. Information will be constantly moving in and out of the network as the situation progresses. Consider an incident involving a person trapped inside a burning structure. Information must be transmitted that tells search teams of locations to search, of changing fire conditions, or to inform that the victim has been located. Each message is vital and yet should not involve lengthy or involved statements. Try to keep it "short and simple (Figure 3.4 on next page)."

The company officer must use the network effectively to order specific actions or tasks to be accomplished. The network is simply a communication process, and a good understanding of how it operates will greatly assist the officer in managing a fireground operation. Effective communication greatly facili-

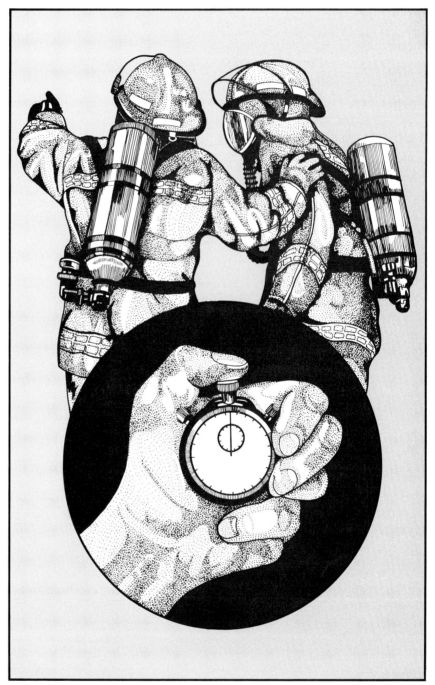

Figure 3.4 Emergency scene communication is vital and must be kept short and simple.

tates operations at the fire scene or other emergency activity and thereby reflects upon the capabilities of the company officer. An effective company officer will be one who understands and is able to select the mode of communication, the needed message, and is able to control the communication network.

Because of the nature of emergency activities and the speed at which they must be performed, fireground communications are almost always verbally transmitted. It is common to use written communications during long campaigns such as forest fires. At the company officer level of communications, almost every incident will necessitate the transmission of orders or information verbally.

When the term "verbal communications" is used, two aspects are involved. There are "face-to-face" communications and radio communications. Both types are parallel because they are used to transmit information and orders. Radio communications will be discussed in Chapter 13, Emergency Operations, Command, and Communications.

FACE-TO-FACE COMMUNICATIONS

Face-to-face or oral communications are generally the most effective means of conveying information. This is because the sender and receiver are speaking directly with each other. It would seem that this method would eliminate misunderstandings, but this is not the case. The reason misunderstandings occur is that people interpret messages differently.

Most people give little thought to what they are saying. This is unfortunate because both the content of the message and the manner in which it is delivered influence the listener's immediate behavior. They also lead the listener to form judgments of the speaker's competence and character. This is very important to the company officer because the message must influence firefighters in a positive manner and leave them with the impression that the officer is indeed competent to lead them.

As simple as face-to-face communication may appear to be, there are several problems that hinder effective transfer of messages. These problems are:

- Officer-firefighter relationships
- Selective hearing
- Words have different meanings
- Emotional context
- Physical barriers

OFFICER-FIREFIGHTER RELATIONSHIPS

When firefighters are assigned to a new or different company, they may need help in learning the methods by which the crew operates. The company officer should open a clear line of communication from the beginning of the relationship to ensure proper and complete transfer of information to the new member. A one-on-one conversation between the company officer and the new company member will be a good way to open this relationship. The second step is that same type of open discussion with other members of the company. Step three would be the new member sharing expectations with the company.

SELECTIVE HEARING

Selective hearing is self-explanatory (Figure 3.5). A person hears only what he or she wants to hear. This is a common problem and something nearly everyone does. There are two major reasons for selective hearing. One, there is too much to hear so the listener only hears what he or she can understand. Two, the listener does not like what is being said, so listens only to the parts of the message he or she agrees with.

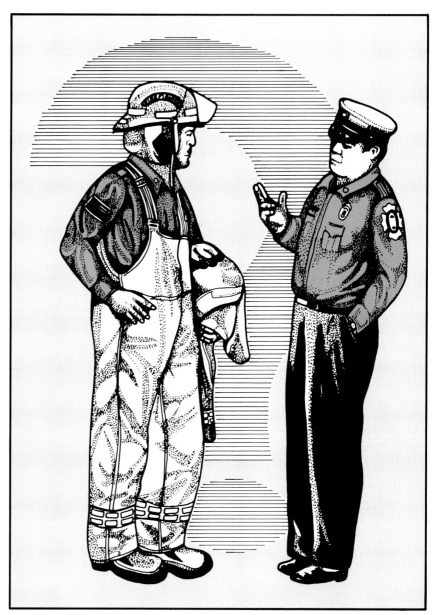

Figure 3.5 A common problem in communication is the act of selective hearing.

WORDS HAVE DIFFERENT MEANINGS

Almost all words in our vocabulary have multiple definitions. People also interpret words differently depending on their background and experiences. These factors present a major communications barrier. The company officer must keep this in mind when dealing with the public. The company officer should use nontechnical terms the public can understand. The officer should also realize that new firefighters may not understand the language of seasoned firefighters. If the officer speaks to the new firefighters in words that can be understood, misinterpretation will be minimized.

EMOTIONAL CONTEXT

The company officer should avoid becoming angry when trying to communicate. The emotional state of an individual greatly influences communication abilities (Figure 3.6). When a person is angry, the message will not be well thought out. Likewise, if the person receiving the message is angry, the message may be misunderstood. In both cases, communication is difficult and will be inaccurate.

Figure 3.6 The emotional state of an individual greatly influences communication.

PHYSICAL BARRIERS

Physical barriers provide communications problems on the fireground. Not everyone can be in contact via radio, so shouting long distances is not uncommon. Another problem is the high noise level on the fireground. These two factors result in difficulties in hearing and speaking clearly. Although not possible in all situations, officers should try to be face to face with the people they are trying to communicate with.

To ensure that messages are received in the manner sent, the speakers should communicate as effectively as possible. Not everyone has excellent communication skills. All people do have the ability to say what they mean and mean what they say. To ensure that what is said is received correctly, the speaker should keep in mind these basic rules of effective spoken messages:

- Be adaptive to the audience (children, professionals)
- Have a specific purpose (to inform/persuade)
- Be brief (get to the point)
- Be focused (stick to the point)
- Be clear (specify meanings)

WRITTEN COMMUNICATIONS

The Memorandum

The memorandum is usually short and to the point, covering only the highlights of one specific subject. The format usually includes the headings To, From, Date, and Subject.

Memos typically formalize a face-to-face conversation or telephone call. They are useful for several reasons:

- Memos transmit exactly the same information to several locations or individuals.
- Memos provide a written record of decisions, requests, or policies.
- Memos provide specific information concerning questions or requests in a somewhat informal manner.

Chief officers generally write more memos than do company officers because formal communication in the fire service hierarchy is more common in a downward than an upward direction. However, there is no reason a company officer should not produce a memo whenever it serves a useful purpose.

Forms

Specific forms are often provided by the fire department and must be used in place of memorandums for specific action. For example, a repair order form brings a basic purpose to the reader's attention upon recognition of the form even before reading what is written on it. Forms also aid in the efficient routing of messages. A repair order form would automatically be sent to the repair shop, whereas a repair memo might sit on someone's desk for a week because the purpose and importance are not evident until the memo is read. Fire officers must fill out forms properly and completely, since all information requested on the form is (or should be) necessary for the receiver.

THE LETTER

Written communications are a reflection of the officer and the department. Letters that are misleading, rude, or poorly written will give the reader a negative impression of the organization. All letters sent out must be grammatically correct, neatly typed, and reflect a positive professional attitude on behalf of the department.

Letters are an effective communication tool if they are written correctly and in a manner appropriate for the subject being discussed. An overly formal or pompous writing style makes the letter writer seem cold; a less formal, but grammatically correct style will accomplish the job in a more friendly manner. Compare the following examples:

Change: It is requested that you send us a copy....

To: I would appreciate your sending.....

or Please send us a copy.............

Both revisions send the same message, but in a manner that is not confusing or difficult to understand. Letters should be concise and to the point without sounding rude.

Excessive wordiness can cause the reader to lose interest or become confused as to the purpose of the letter. On the other hand, a letter that is too brief can read like a telegram. The letter should be checked after the first draft for wordiness or inadequate explanation. Several examples follow:

Change: This is to acknowledge receipt of your letter...

To: Thank you for your letter......

Change: I would like to express my appreciation and thanks

To: Thank you for......

or I appreciate your assistance.....

Letters that are too brief will give the impression of rudeness, particularly when it is necessary to refuse a request. It is important to give a complete answer or explanation to all requests.

The appearance of a letter is as important as the style because it is a critical part of the overall impression given to the reader. All letters should be neatly typed without obvious mistakes or corrections. It is assumed that a letter signed by an officer has been either written or proofread by the officer. The reader will interpret the letter's appearance as an example of the officer's professionalism and attention to detail.

A helpful consideration for every letter writer is to realize that the reader will be reading the letter with interest. Let the letter be a substitute for an actual conversation; a natural and sincere expression of thoughts. To accomplish this, the writer needs to develop an attitude of "you" toward the reader. Maintain an awareness of the reader's impressions, thoughts, and feelings that may result from a letter.

The combined use of natural expression of thoughts and a grammatically correct format will provide a good foundation for clear expression that will reflect positively on the company officer and the department (Figure 3.7).

Format Of Letters

It is important to consider how a letter is structured. To be consistent, all letters sent out from the department should follow the same format. There are a few rules of accepted practice that should be followed. They are as follows:

THE HEADING

The heading is usually the department's letterhead or logo. The heading should contain the return address and telephone number of the writer so that a response can be returned if necessary. Always have the entire address written out. For example, do not use "St." or "Rd." for street or road.

DATE LINE

The date line is two lines below the heading, either on the left- or right-hand margin. Either location is acceptable. Again, write out all information such as the month and date. The proper way to express the date of the letter is, for example, July 6, 1989 or 6 July 1989. Do not use the method 7/6/89 or 7-6-89.

INSIDE ADDRESS

Allow four spaces below the date line for the inside address. The inside address must include the name, title, and address of the person receiving the letter. If the person holds an official title within the company, such as vice president, captain, or manager, the appropriate title follows the person's name.

SHERWOOD FIRE DEPARTMENT

Station 17
32 Morris Road
Sherwood, Idaho
83705
(208)744-9132

October 16,1990

Mr. Paul Marsden
32 Fox Hill Road
Sherwood, Idaho 83705

Dear Mr. Marsden:

This letter is in reply to your letter of October 10th
advising us of the careless disposal of gasoline-soaked rags
at the Lyons Gasoline Station on Underwood Avenue. Thank you
for reporting this matter to us.

You will be relieved to learn that the day after we received your letter, we dispatched two fire officers to the
Lyons Gasoline Station to inspect the premises and to investigate the station's method of discarding used rags. All atten-
dants at the station were carefully instructed by our firefighters in the proper procedures for disposal of such rags.
In addition, a warning has been issued to the manager of the
Lyons Station putting him on notice that if he does not comply
with the instructions, he will be in violation of Order #3652
of this city.

A return inspection of the gasoline station is scheduled
for October 25th.

Again, I thank you for taking the time and trouble to
write to us about this matter. Your generous efforts have
surely contributed to eliminating yet another fire hazard in
our community.

Sincerely,

Art Pepper
Captain

Figure 3.7 An example of a business letter.

SUBJECT LINE

Allow two lines below the inside address or two lines below the salutation for the subject line. The subject line is used to focus the reader's attention on the content of the letter. If the subject line is above the salutation, it is not necessary to use the word "subject." To avoid confusion for the reader, however, "subject" should be written if the subject line is below the salutation line. The subject line is not necessary for all communications, but may be used in certain situations.

SALUTATION

This is the point where the writer addresses the reader (Dear Mr...). Avoid excessive salutations such as "My Dear Sir." Whatever salutation is used, it should contain the person's name and title as it appears in the inside address. If the name is unknown, the common practice is to use a subject line.

THE BODY

For appearance, there are some helpful spacing techniques that will make the letter more presentable. Average letters should be single-spaced between lines and double-spaced between paragraphs. Shorter letters should be double-spaced between lines and triple-spaced between paragraphs.

Some additional tips: Do not split a date or a person's name between lines. Where there is a need to continue on another page, the last paragraph on the first page should contain at least two lines. If two lines will not fit on the page, start the paragraph on the next page. Always carry at least two lines of the body text over to the second page; do not use a continuation page to type only the letter's closing. The second page should be typed on plain paper of quality equivalent to the letterhead. The second page should have a heading with the recipient's name, page number, and date. The heading may go in the upper left hand corner or across the page.

CLOSURE

Space two lines after the last paragraph of the body for the complimentary close. Try to choose a simple closing such as "Sincerely." Again, the key is to be concise and appropriate.

SIGNATURE

The last spacing requirement is to leave four spaces below the closing and type your name, and title if appropriate.

By combining a correct format with proper tone and style, the company officer can communicate in a professional and effective manner. The company officer who uses written expression well has another asset to rely on in managing a fire company.

REPORT WRITING

The mere mention of report writing often brings out visions of slaving over a report that was due yesterday. This concept of report writing can be positively changed if the officer follows some basic ideas and understands the organizational importance of a good report. This section provides some helpful guidelines for completing a well-organized report.

Reports are necessary to document fire prevention activities, investigations, and injuries to civilians and firefighters. As a manager, the responsibilities of a company officer include the ability to effectively handle report writing. Keep in mind that any written report is a reflection of the company and of the officer.

The majority of report writing done by the company officer consists of completing standard department forms and various log books. Reports are designed to provide vital and useful information to the department. Care should be taken to make each report neat in appearance and legible to the reader. This often requires that the report be typewritten or printed by a computer. The content of the report is even more important than its appearance. Information within the report should be delivered in a manner that is easily understood and not misleading (Figure 3.8 on next page).

To produce a well-written report requires the use of complete sentences, proper grammar, and appropriate use of words. These are basic writing techniques that apply to any type of report but plague many report writers. It is easy to write a report and have it appear to communicate the necessary information, only to find that the reader does not understand the report due to improper grammar or incomplete sentences. Two methods to overcome these problem areas of report writing are to practice writing skills and to have a second person proofread the report.

Misspelled words reflect poorly on the writer and will make the reader question the report's technical content. Any question about the spelling of a word should be settled by consulting a dictionary. Run-on or partial sentences make it difficult to understand the writer's meaning; it is always good writing practice to use short, clear sentences. Consult a good, easy-to-use style manual for correct word usage and punctuation.

Too many reports are plagued by misspelled words, poor punctuation, and inappropriate words. Writers sometimes fall into a habit of using unnecessary words or words with duplicate meanings. Always try to use words that identify exactly the meaning intended, and avoid words that may give the reader a different impression.

On page 61 are some easy-to-see examples of unnecessary words. Word choice is an important consideration when writing effective, concise communications.

SHERWOOD FIRE DEPARTMENT

Station 17
32 Morris Road
Sherwood, Idaho
83705
(208)744-9132

INVESTIGATIVE REPORT #165

To: *(Give name and title of appropriate superior in your locality.)*
From: *(Give your own name and title.)*
Subject: Investigation of
Date:

SUMMARY OF INCIDENT UNDER INVESTIGATION
        (Include time and date of occurrence and company or
        station involved.)

INFORMATION LEARNED FROM INVESTIGATION
        (Organize the information according to common subject
        matter, and present it in paragraph form, grouping and tying together related
        facts. Use complete sentences, proper grammar, and correct spellings.)

CAUSE OF ACCIDENT

RESPONSIBILITY FOR ACCIDENT
        (Organization, department,or individual responsible.)
RECOMMENDATIONS
        (Include whether further investigation should be undertaken.)

        Respectfully submitted,

        (Write your signature here.)
        (Give your rank and company here.)

Figure 3.8 An example of a model investigation report.

Example	*Should Be*
first of all	first
the actual truth	the truth
in the meantime	meanwhile
was definitely dangerous	was dangerous
for a period of two weeks	for two weeks
at this point in time	at this time; now

Taking time to prepare and adequately write a report will allow the opportunity to catch common writing mistakes. After the report is grammatically correct and proper use of words and appropriate punctuation have been assured, effort should be devoted to making the report neat in appearance.

Using these basic report writing guidelines will enable officers to present themselves and their company in a positive and professional manner. Because a company officer's position is management, and oral and written communications are an integral part of everyday activity, it is crucial that clear and effective communications become second nature. It is beyond the scope of this manual to fully teach professional business communications; therefore, it is recommended any individual in a fire service management position complete a business communication course.

INFORMAL COMMUNICATIONS
Grapevine

All fire departments have an official system of communications. Most often this system is synonymous with the chain of command. Every day the bulk of organizational information is transmitted via this system. In addition to this formal system, almost every department has an equally active informal system of communication. This informal system is most often called the grapevine system. The grapevine is a social communications network that transmits the organization's social news and, often, official information in an informal manner.

In general, the grapevine system is a communications system; however, it is not a preferred method of transmitting official communications (Figure 3.9). In some instances, official news traveling through the grapevine can have extremely detrimental effects upon the morale and operations of a department. The basic flaws in the grapevine system that make it unacceptable from the department's point of view are:

- There is no method of ensuring that inaccurate or false information can be distinguished from official information. A rumor has the same validity as official information.

Figure 3.9 A grapevine system is a real communications medium but not a preferred method.

- There is no way to ensure that complete information is transmitted. Often, in cases of disputes, only the information supporting the speaker's point of view is presented, or if presented, the facts are out of context.

- There is no way to ensure information is not slanted because of personal bias of the speaker.

- There is no method to allow for clarification of information or correction of misinformation through the system.

- There is no method to prevent confidential disclosures that can embarrass either the department or individuals.

Some officers and department officials attempt to reduce the passing of departmental business through the grapevine. Others simply pretend that it does not exist. In these instances, the bad effects of the grapevine tend to be maximized. This is because the officials are then completely excluded from the grapevine and have no way to monitor the information content. The only effective approach to minimizing the effects of the grapevine is to recognize its existence and accept its inevitability. Only after these two decisions are made can measures be employed to minimize the bad effects.

> **The single most effective method of minimizing the effects of the grapevine is to provide adequate flow of official information.**

Rumors develop and grow when the members of the organization have a desire to understand a situation, but the facts are ambiguous or concealed. The official information flow should be set in a regular fashion and continue to produce information regardless of the interest expressed by the employees. A good method for this regular flow is a daily or weekly bulletin that is printed and posted.

Information that tends to require the closest attention to prevent grapevine distortion is information about:

- Promotions

- Hirings and firings

- Lay-offs, transfers, or shift changes

- Disciplinary actions

- Equipment expenditures

- Accidents or injuries

In areas involving these topics, extra care taken to provide current and correct information is a necessity. As soon as is practical after a decision is made, the information should be made available. Often, for major decisions, a concise "news release" is provided at the time of the decision. This release provides the essential information concerning the decision. Copies of news releases should be forwarded to all stations for posting. For minor decisions, a memorandum may serve the same purpose.

SUMMARY

Communication involves much more than mere "talking." For communication to be effective, a message must be sent and understood. Communication is a process that involves the sender, the message, the medium, the receiver, and feedback from the receiver.

Listening is also an important concept in communications. To receive the message with the meaning intended, the listener must take an active role and be alert.

The communication process involves the use of several types of formal communications. Written policies and procedures are plans for dealing with recurring problems. Fireground orders have a different nature than regular orders. Due to the danger involved, company officers must be able to issue fireground orders in a clear, concise, and complete manner. Fireground communication involves both "face-to-face" communications and radio communications (discussed in Chapter 13). The company officer must also know how and when to use the various types of written communications. Among these are the memorandum, forms, the letter, and reports.

Informal communication is also important to the company officer. The grapevine is basically a social communications network. It can be used to receive information but should never be used to transmit information.

SUPPLEMENTAL READINGS

Effective Supervisory Practices. 2nd ed. Washington D.C.: International City Management Association, 1984.

Gratz, David B. *Fire Department Management: Scope and Method*. Beverly Hills: Glencoe Press, 1972.

Leadership In The Fire Service. 1st ed. Stillwater, Okla.: Fire Protection Publications, Oklahoma State University, 1967.

Management in the Fire Service. Didactic Systems, Inc. Boston: National Fire Protection Association, 1977.

4

The Company
As A Group

LESSON OBJECTIVES

After completing this chapter and related *Student Guide* applications, company officer candidates should be able to:

- Recall the definition of *group*.

- Distinguish between formal and informal groups.

- Recall the five essential elements of all groups.

- Explain how Maslow's five levels of need relate to the company group.

- Recall the purpose of transactional analysis.

- Explain the three ego states in the transactional analysis theory.

- Explain what transactional analysts mean by *strokes* and *stamp collecting*.

- Recognize factors that determine effective group interaction.

This chapter addresses NFPA 1021,
Standard for Fire Officer Professional Qualifications (1987):
2-3.1	3-1
	3-2.1

Chapter 4
The Company As A Group

A fire company can be described in many ways: as a unit of a fire department, a suborganization, or a subdivision of the fire department. The one common element of these definitions is that they imply that the company is a group of firefighters. Society is composed of a multitude of formal and informal groups. A group is defined as: Two or more persons who interact with regard to common goals. The goals may or may not be explicitly stated (Figure 4.1).

The explicitness of the stated goals indicates the formality of the group. Formal groups usually define common goals in writing. A fire company is a formal group of firefighters who interact to meet common goals as outlined by departmental policy. Informal groups, on the other hand, define common goals informally. A friendship can be described as an informal group: two persons who interact with the common goal of friendship.

Within each formal group, it is common for informal groups to form. For instance, two co-workers in a fire company may form an informal group with the unstated goal of mutual friendship. Many potential informal organizations exist within each formal group. These organizations are limited only by the common interests of the individual members of the company. Informal groups most often form around hobbies such as boating or fishing, political interests, social interests, religious beliefs, and sports activities.

The important point to remember concerning informal groups is that each informal group will have an effect upon the formal group, the company. The effect may be good if the members encourage each other to support the company. The effect may be negative if the individuals regard their informal group's goals as more important than the goals of the company.

Figure 4.1 A group is two or more persons who interact with regard to some common goal.

Research into the relationship of formal and informal groups has brought to light two important facts:

- Informal groups form within all formal groups.

- The informal group may have greater influence on the productivity and success of the formal group than does any other factor.

An officer's understanding of the elements of group dynamics is vital since this connection has been found between informal group support and formal group success or failure. The company officer's role in the group becomes one of meshing the goals of the formal and informal groups. In pursuing this role, the company officer directs behavior to meet the goals of both the company and the informal group.

The company officer is the leader of the formal group by the authority vested in the position by the department; however, the company officer's position in the informal group, and the ability to deal with the informal group, is determined by group dynamics. For this reason, the company officer must learn to work within the relationships of the company.

The dynamics of a group include complex social forces that act within and upon every group and that together determine group behavior. Groups have relatively static aspects such as their name (for example, Ladder Company 7), their overall functions, and perhaps a fixed number of members. But every group also has dynamic aspects. Groups are always changing, interacting, and reacting. Changes in group makeup, modifications of organizational structure, and specific events all bring about group change. The directions in which groups move are determined by forces exerted from both within and outside the group. A complete explanation of group dynamics is too complex to be attempted within the limits of this publication, but addressing the subject and creating an awareness of group dynamics can help the company officer manage the company. This awareness will also help the officer participate in informal groups.

GROUP DYNAMICS

The group formation of a fire company is not significantly different from the formation of any other formal or informal group. Every group, including the fire company, tends to meet the five essential elements of a group. The members must:

- Have a common binding interest

- Have a vital group image

- Have a sense of continuity

- Have a shared set of moral values

- Recognize different roles within the group

The study of the effects of these five basic elements can be described as the study of group dynamics. This study involves recognizing the internal and external pressures that affect these elements, and learning to deal with the elements.

Common Binding Interests

Every person has the common interest of being human, but few groups are formed on this basis. The interest that holds a group together must be more binding. This means that the members feel that the common interest is important enough to their own needs to hold membership in the group. An example of this would be a community in which residents of a three block area were surveyed, and a representative for each residence indicated a need to reduce fire losses in that neighborhood. This demonstrated that they all had a common interest. However, the interest was not strong enough to mold the individuals into a group, and no group ever formed to promote fire safety in that neighborhood.

Interests of individuals change and their participation in a group may change. In life, certain groups have interests that are binding to the individual only for a given period of time. Take, for instance, the young boy, Tom. Tom's interest at age seven is strong toward Cub Scouts, and Tom is an active member of that group. Soon, Tom outgrows the Scouts and becomes involved in baseball. During Tom's high school years, he is bound by a common social interest with other high school members. Today, Tom is a firefighter and is part of Engine Number 6. The common interest of fighting fires in District 6 binds that group together. For this reason, the company officer must view interest on the part of firefighters as transitory. That is, the company officer must strive to maintain the firefighters' interests in the company if the interest begins to lessen (Figure 4.2).

Figure 4.2 The officer must work to keep the firefighter interested in meeting the goals of the company and the department.

Vital Group Image

The members of the group must share a vital group image, that is, the members of the group must recognize the existence of their group and take pride in it. This pride will result in high morale.

For instance, such a recognition would be evident if the neighbors in the first example all decided to write to their congressional representative about fire safety. This conceivably could be regarded as a binding interest, but the members of the neighborhood still view themselves as individuals, not as a group. Until such time as the members see themselves as a group, the ability of the group to be successful is nominal.

The group image of the members, in addition to being essential to the conception of the group, is one of the greatest influences on the success of the group. A group tends to produce in accord with its own group image. Groups that have a positive self-image tend to be better achievers. This positive self-image is sometimes called esprit de corps. This French term pertains to the common spirit existing in the members of a group and inspiring enthusiasm. Groups that have low group images tend to be poor producers.

Sense Of Continuity

The sense of continuity of a group is very important. If the members of the group do not perceive that continued existence of the group is probable, their commitment to the group is very shallow. By disturbing the members' sense of continuity, the group can be fragmented, and the members will begin to act more individually. Think about the staff of a fire department shift as a group, and imagine that the battalion chief is transferred. The workers on the shift often lose their sense of continuity because they are not sure what the next shift supervisor will be like. The members begin to become very individualistic and perhaps even territorial. Generally, during the transition from one shift commander to the next, production with coordinated effort decreases.

A change in leadership is one way to disrupt the sense of continuity, but many actions can result in a similar disruption. Other common actions are shift changes, policy changes, labor-generated conflicts, serious injury or death within the group, or any other traumatic occurrence.

Moral Values

Moral values have developed as part of the organizational structure of all common groups. They are usually a composite of individual morality. Philosophies of individuals surface as various subjects are approached on a day-to-day basis in normal interaction within the group structure. The moral philosophy of a group is usually modified by a change in the group membership. This change in attitude occurs gradually and is related to group acceptance of the new members' value structure.

Group values are also affected by the traditional values of the organization. The moral philosophy of the organization will normally be reflected in the attitudes and morality of groups within the organization.

As an example, organizational morals of a fire department dictate that firefighters are trustworthy and honest. It should not be an issue for members of an elite public service group such as this to enter structures where there is high priced merchandise or other valuables. With effective leadership and guidance, that organizational moral standard will also be a primary moral objective of a fire company with that organization.

The overall values of a group also depend on when members of that group are "value programmed." In his electronic lecture series, Dr. Morris Massey says, "At approximately ten, probably 90% of our gut level value system locks in to be used to filter through the world for the rest of our lives." Thinking back to when an individual was growing up and identifying the significant factors and events during those years can help answer questions about that person's current values. Different age groups have different values, and they are a product of the individual's family, friends, religion, school, geography, family income, and exposure to the electronic media.

A dramatic change may occur in people's "gut level" value systems during their lives. A "significant emotional event" may change behavior or alter beliefs. A "brush with death," for example, may change the philosophy and modify the values of an entire company.

Recognition of variations in values through different age groups is an important step in managing people. The company officer must realize that differences do exist and make provisions for those differences.

Different Roles Within The Group

Within each group, the members either formally or informally select different individuals to act in different roles. With formal groups, the leader is either assigned or elected. With informal groups, the leader is acknowledged through social recognition. Obviously, the official leader of the fire company is not necessarily the informal leader. It is desirable when the company officer is the leader in both the formal and the informal groups, but this is not always the case. The company officer must recognize this and learn to deal within the group in both roles.

The Company Officer's Combination Of Roles

A company officer functions in roles both on and off the job. At work, firefighters expect the officer to fulfill the role of supervisor. At home, the officer's roles may include spouse, parent, bowling team member, or church member. Most people play several roles simultaneously. For example, the company officer is superior and subordinate at the same time: superior for the company, subordinate to higher management.

Role Expectation

As mentioned, the fire officer's subordinates expect the officer to be a supervisor. Officers and firefighters alike are guided in performing their duties by what others expect of that position. This is called role expectation. A fire officer's perception of the role is influenced by the role expectations of the formal organization, by group members, and by the officer's own ideas of what it means to be a company officer (Figure 4.3).

It is important for the officer to realize that the ability to positively influence the group is not dependent upon holding the informal leadership role. Generally, any role within the group

Figure 4.3 The officer fills many roles in a fire department company structure. Many roles are defined by self-perception and some by how others perceive the officer.

can be used to help guide the group. Therefore, the officer must be aware of the informal role held within the group, and learn to use the influence of that role. The most detrimental action the officer can take is to separate from the informal group. When this happens, the officer has no potential influence except from the formal perspective. Constant evaluation of the group by the company officer is critical. The officer must know his or her place in the informal group and recognize the position of other company members in this important structure.

Rules And Guidelines

Each group has its own rules and guidelines. For the formal fire company, the rules and guidelines are departmental policies and procedures. In some cases, the informal group will develop its own rules and guidelines. The informal rules can be much stronger or persuasive than the formal rules. The traditions of the group are one form of informal rules or guidelines, but the total system may be very complicated and diverse. Regardless of the complexity, the company officer must learn to recognize these rules and guidelines. The company officer must decide which informal rules or guidelines are acceptable to the formal group. Then, either through the informal or formal role, the officer must modify informal rules that tend to be unacceptable.

For example, Captain Harper took over Engine 25 in 1985. The membership of the company remained much the same for four years, but in 1989, Firefighter Rollins, the engineer, became an officer. The senior firefighter took over the engineer position, and a rookie firefighter joined the company. Other members of the company slowly began playing small practical jokes on the rookie. At first the jokes were funny, but soon Captain Harper had to intervene. This was the first rookie Captain Harper had join her company, and she realized that the informal rules required the rookie to be hazed. However, this was unacceptable to the formal group, and Captain Harper had to use her influence to change the informal rules.

The Group As Individuals

Understanding the five basic elements of group dynamics enables the company officer to begin understanding the forces behind the factors influencing the fire company. There is also an additional underlying fact that is equally important: The total production of the group is determined by the interaction of the group members on an individual basis. In other words, when attempting to analyze how or why a group is acting in a certain fashion, the individual relationships within the group must be studied. To begin such a study, a review of the basic human motivators can be helpful.

People interact in different ways and from different motivations. The psychologist, Abraham Maslow, developed a widely accepted theory that outlines the basic motivational factors. This theory, called Maslow's Hierarchy of Needs, attempts to explain why individuals behave in the manner they do. In his theory, Maslow contends that all human behavior is motivated by a drive to attain specific human needs (Figure 4.4).

The attainment of these needs is believed to be a progressive action; that is, the basic needs must be attained before higher needs will be sought. Thus, a pyramid of needs is developed with the fundamental needs (life support) as a base and social needs (acceptance) at the top.

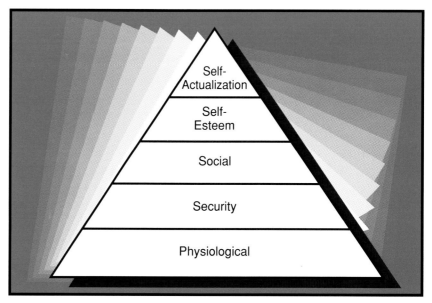

Figure 4.4 Maslow originated the Hierarchy of Needs. Generally, individuals strive for the higher needs after the lower needs have been secured.

Basic Physiological Needs

The basic physiological needs for all humans as listed by Maslow are food, water, air, clothing, and shelter. These items are generally believed to be basic for survival. The most common method of securing the bulk of these needs in our society is through an occupation. People work for salaries that they spend to secure these commodities. Only after obtaining these basic necessities will the individual seek fulfillment of the higher level of needs. The next level of need, according to the theory, is the need for safety and security.

Safety And Security

Safety and security are primarily insulation or protection from events that might interrupt an individual's ability to continue meeting the basic physiological needs. After an individual learns to provide for basic survival, there is a tendency to use earnings for developing safety and security. This development might be in the form of a savings account or investment. Some other forms of safety and security in the working world are insurance policies, workmen's compensation provisions, and labor organization benefits. Employers often provide fringe benefit packages that guarantee worker security.

These benefit packages are almost universal in the modern world, although some are more lavish than others. In most of the industrial world today, the fulfillment of these first two levels of human needs are almost guaranteed by extensive social welfare programs. This is especially true in the United States and Canada. For this reason, the predominance of a firefighter's drive will be to attain higher levels of needs. The next level of the need hierarchy is that of social needs.

Belonging And Social Activity

Belonging and social activity are those needs an individual attempts to attain in regard to other human relationships. These needs include the need for attention and the need to belong to a group. It is at this level that the basis of informal group interactions is formed. Each member within a group uses his or her position in the group to attain belonging and social activity needs. For this reason, the group is capable of exerting peer pressure on an individual who fails to comply with the group guidelines. This pressure is exerted by the group in refusing to fulfill the individual's need for belonging and social activity.

The potential influence that the group can have upon individuals in the group can be the difference between the success or failure of a formal organization. If the members in the group influence members to be achievers, then the company officer's job is much easier. If the group members tend to pressure other members to be mediocre producers, however, the company officer will certainly face some motivational problems. The type of pressure that the group exerts is extremely important for the officer to monitor.

Esteem And Status

Once belonging and social activity needs have been attained, Maslow's theory contends that the individual will strive to meet esteem and status needs. These needs involve ego fulfillment through individual recognition, status, peer respect, and achievement. When esteem needs are met, the individual's self-image is bolstered, and the person's sense of personal worth is heightened.

The company officer should strive to recognize how the firefighters in the company view themselves and attempt to help them develop or strengthen their sense of self-respect. The Strokes and Stamp Collecting section later in this chapter will provide more information on this subject.

Self-Actualization And Fulfillment

At the top of Maslow's hierarchy are self-actualization and fulfillment. These needs are fulfilled when a person feels that the limits of his or her ability have been reached. Generally, individuals reach this level in respect to a certain job or achievement. For example, self-actualization is usually attained when a firefighter saves a child or when a company efficiently extinguishes a potentially major fire. At these times, individuals will fulfill the self-actualization need, but soon, possibly at the next call, the individual will be striving to meet it again.

Application Of Maslow's Need Model

Studying group interactions on an individual basis is much easier when examined in respect to Maslow's need model. Of course, different individuals will strive to receive fulfillment of different need levels from the group. Unfortunately, there is no simple test the company officer can perform to decide which needs each individual in the company is striving to meet. Nevertheless, the hierarchy of needs can provide some general guidelines.

Social Need Fulfillment

Social needs are based on a person's desire to belong and to be accepted. The company officer's position in the formal group can help members of the group attain these social needs. The supervisor can do this by studying the five elements of a group and assisting the company members in achieving these elements.

It is important that all members of a fire company be challenged by their work. In the process, the individual must receive a feeling of satisfaction about the work when it is completed. Members must be able to see their contributions to the company effort satisfying some of their individual objectives as well as those of the company and the department. Therefore, the company officer should attempt to mesh the interest of the firefighter with that of the department. One way to accomplish this is by reviewing departmental goals during company training, especially with respect to how the company fits into the overall department plan. Before such sessions, the officer should consult departmental policies, standard operating procedures, job descriptions, and task analysis to help clarify the purpose of the company. Providing copies of such documents may help firefighters develop interest. Ideally, after such a session, the firefighter should be able to state: "Yes; there is a plan, and I am an important part of that plan." Department members at every level should be included in revisions of departmental policies, job analysis, and standard operating procedures. This ensures a vested interest in the overall goals of the organization.

The officer can do much in the way of developing a group image. Of all the methods of bolstering the ability of the company to meet social needs, this area has perhaps the most potential. To begin this reinforcement, the officer must first accept the group concept. After that, methods of reinforcement become plentiful. Plaques can be made and hung referring to the attributes of the company (Figure 4.5). Baseball caps and T-shirts for off-duty use can be purchased and distributed to emphasize the social group.

There are many methods that could achieve similar advantages. The application of these methods can be guided by simply examining the five essential elements of a group and using techniques that strengthen the social needs.

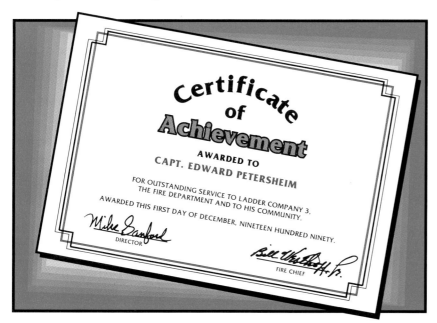

Figure 4.5 The group image of a company can be changed in many ways. Certificates, plaques, company hats, shirts, jackets, and patches all reinforce membership.

Esteem And Status Application

Maslow's fourth need is the need for esteem and status. Esteem and status are often thought of as simply ego fulfillment. This may be defined as:

> An individual's attempts to influence events so that external feedback matches the individual's self-image.

This might be demonstrated by the firefighter who believes he or she is the most knowledgeable person in the station. This person is always telling others how to do things and trying to receive recognition. Whether the firefighter is trying to reinforce the image to cover up inadequacies, or for some other psychological reason, these actions still attempt to reinforce the individual's self-image. More simply, it does not matter why he or she is trying to reinforce the image, only that the actions tend to do so. Armed with that information, the company officer can begin to understand how the group interacts with that individual.

This principle might be illustrated by firefighters who perceive themselves as being valuable assets to the community fire defense system (self-image). These firefighters would likely attend special training sessions, join groups with professional interests, take on additional duties, or participate in other related affairs. As people respond to these activities, it reinforces the self-image of the firefighters. Some firefighters may compensate for feelings of inadequacy or dissatisfaction by acting in a similar fashion; in both cases, the reinforcement acts to bolster the individuals' self-image.

TRANSACTIONAL ANALYSIS

One method of examining esteem and status fulfillment is through transactional analysis. Transactional analysis is a method used for analyzing human behavior and communication between individuals. The transactional analysis theory presents one way of looking at ego involvement in the transmittal of messages. The theory maintains that a person has three ego states—parent, child, and adult. These ego states vary in strength at all times.

The parent ego state is the evaluative part of a person. This side of one's character is composed of things learned from parents, teachers, and other authority figures. It is the parent ego state that usually has an answer for everything and says "follow the rules and work hard." There are two kinds of parent ego states. One, the nurturing parent, shows understanding and caring about other people. The other, the critical parent, makes people feel that they, and their behavior, are unacceptable.

The child ego state represents an individual's emotional side. This ego state is the emotional, rebellious, carefree, and creative side of a person. There are two kinds of child ego states. The first, the happy child, has a behavior that is not disruptive to others or to the environment. The second, the destructive child, has behavior that can be disruptive to others or destructive to the environment.

The adult ego state is logical, rational, and responsive. The adult's decisions are based on information received from the parent, the child, and the world in general.

In transactional analysis, each communication between people is called a transaction. These transactions have their origin in one of the three ego states, depending upon which state is dominant at the moment the transaction is made. Sets of transactions can be either complementary, crossed, or hidden.

The transaction is complementary when the ego state in one person receives a message from the ego state it addressed in another person. For example:

> Firefighter Brown: "That's not the right way to do that. Let me show you how it's supposed to be done." (Parent to Child)
>
> Firefighter Thomas: "Will you get off my back. I'll do it when I get ready." (Child to Parent)

This transaction is complementary although the interactions seem to be somewhat hostile. The fact that Firefighter Brown was interacting from a parent-to-child ego state, and that Firefighter Thomas's response reinforced Brown's image of himself as the parent makes it a complementary transaction. Complementary transactions are not necessarily positive or pleasant, but they reinforce the roles the individuals have assumed.

There are three basic forms of complementary transactions. The first, and perhaps most productive, is the adult-to-adult transaction (Figure 4.6). Firefighter A communicates with Firefighter B as an adult. Firefighter B responds as an adult reinforcing Firefighter A's self-image as an adult. The second complementary transaction is the parent-to-child transaction, as seen in the example of Firefighters Brown and Thomas. The third type of complementary transaction is a child-to-child trans-

Figure 4.6 Of all the transactions, the adult to adult is usually the most productive.

action. Complementary transactions between adult and parent or adult and child do not typically exist in mature individuals, because an adult ego will tend to address an adult ego. Additionally, parent-to-parent complementary transactions seldom occur because the parent almost always addresses the child.

Crossed transactions occur when the ego states are not complementary. Such transactions would be those between a parent or child ego and an adult ego. Crossed transactions cause additional problems because the individuals' egos become damaged or unfulfilled. In these instances, friction can develop between individuals. Crossed transactions will usually block communications. An example of a crossed transaction is Firefighter Brown initially communicating from the adult ego state, but Firefighter Thomas remaining in the child ego state:

> Firefighter Brown: "Tom, it looks like you are having a little trouble with that. Would you like me to help?" (Adult to Adult)
>
> Firefighter Thomas: "Will you get off my back. I'll do it when I get ready." (Child to Parent)

Transactions can be hidden when there is an unspoken meaning attached to a message. For example, a group of firefighters might be resting at the station after battling a commercial fire for several hours. A firefighter was critically injured in the fire. The firefighters sit quietly awaiting news of their friend. Firefighter Jones has known the injured firefighter since elementary school. They are like brothers. Firefighter Brown might say to Firefighter Jones: "Bob, I'll bet I can beat you in a pool game," (Child to Child). Here, the real meaning of the communication is hidden. Although Brown is speaking from a child ego state, he is issuing a communication from the adult state. He might be saying, "Bob, we're all worried about our friend, but that is not going to help. Let's try to relax and take our minds off of it for awhile."

The supervisor or company officer who can recognize the different ego states and transactions between people will be able to deal with the firefighters more effectively. The officer can use knowledge of transactional analysis to help remain calm and reasonable with the adult ego state in control, while others are temporarily dominated by the parent or child ego.

STROKES AND STAMP COLLECTING

Transactional analysts use the term stroke to mean a feeling that results from a transaction. If a person receives a pleasant or positive feeling (one that reinforces the ego) from the transaction, the person is receiving a positive stroke. If the feeling is unpleasant (one that fails to reinforce the ego), a negative stroke has been received. For example, a friendly greeting or praise for a job well done are positive strokes. Unfair criticism, abuse, or an unfriendly attitude are negative strokes.

All strokes are converted into stamps. Stamp collecting is a term used to describe the process of collecting strokes. When one person provides another with several positive strokes, eventually the person receiving these positive strokes will "cash them in" or, in other words, do something positive in return for the other person. The same principle applies to the collection of negative strokes. The person collecting negative strokes will sooner or later reciprocate, and some negative action will take place, perhaps resulting in an argument. Often, negative action will be in the form of sabotage of another individual's efforts.

The most important point of strokes and stamp collecting is that people tend to pursue actions for which they receive positive strokes. They tend to avoid actions or individuals that give them negative strokes. It should be noted that if no strokes are given, usually an individual will try to receive at least a negative stroke. Negative strokes are usually better than no strokes at all. The company officer should work at learning to "stroke" individuals. These strokes can be used to reinforce members of the group in the actions that benefit the company. In addition, because of the reciprocal quality of stroking and the fact that it can be contagious, such actions often tend to build strong groups.

Socioeconomic Background As A Group Factor

Class and caste are partial determinants of behavior in every society. Even in a country like the United States, whose Declaration of Independence proclaims everyone to be equal, society is stratified into classes by such factors as education, income, inherited wealth, occupation, ancestral status, and race. The legal and moral attempt to abolish racial discrimination, for example, as a factor in social stratification has met with only partial success. Life position in the predominant social structure of the United States and Canada is not as rigidly determined as in some societies. However, many—if not most—people tend to identify with some perceived socioeconomic group based on such factors as those previously named. They also tend to see others as either fellow members or outsiders. Although the criteria that identifies one as belonging to a particular class may be extremely subjective and open to widely varying interpretation, perceived social status can have an effect on interpersonal relations.

Leadership of a group depends to a varying degree upon the willingness of its members to follow the leader designated by the formal organization. Basing action on knowledge about the typical behavior of individual group members can help an officer.

Acceptance of the leader chosen, not by group members but by the organization's promotion system, is somewhat dependent on the socioeconomic class of the individual group members. That is, the socioeconomic class with which a member might identify seems to determine at least partly how that person will relate to the leader. Of course, the social and economic background of the leader also enters into the picture. Therefore, it can be safely assumed that the leader's behavior toward followers, and their behavior toward the leader, are partially determined by the socioeconomic backgrounds of both leader and group members.

Early in life, individuals realize that they belong to various groups. These groups, from the individual's perspective, are "in-groups." If, for instance, one is of Catholic belief, then all other religious groups are out-groups.

From this fundamental polarization, certain attitudes begin to show. Unfortunately, many people seem to comprehend their in-group memberships largely in terms of the differences, real and imagined, from members of out-groups. The action of thinking of themselves as distinctly different from out-group members often results in the rejection of out-groups. This rejection is expressed mostly in three ways: verbal rejection (usually when the intended victim is not present), physical avoidance, and discrimination in the form of prejudging out-group members in a generally unfavorable light.

With reference only to people, prejudice is a feeling, favorable or unfavorable, toward a person that is not based on actual experience with that particular individual. Usually, prejudice is used in a negative sense. Prejudice then means that an individual judges a person unfavorably without basing the judgment on experience with that person. Prejudice in the negative sense can lead to acts of discrimination. Discrimination has been suffered by people because of their skin color, religious beliefs, national or ethnic background, sex, sexual preference, or political beliefs. These are irrational bases for judging an individual before knowing that individual.

Take a hypothetical case involving skin color and Firefighter Adams: Firefighter Adams did not believe blacks were inferior inherently, but he did feel that most blacks had a lack of cultural stimulation, which made them culturally inferior. Firefighter Adams met Firefighter Jones, a black, when he was transferred to a new station. Firefighter Adams assumed that Firefighter Jones would be culturally inferior. In the following weeks, Firefighter Adams was often surprised at how much Firefighter Jones knew about the arts, classical music, and literature. Eventually, Firefighter Adams found out from an associate that Firefighter Jones had a college degree in humanities.

Firefighter Adams had failed to recognize that although some blacks may be culturally limited, so may some whites, some Mexican Americans, and some Orientals. He should have realized that it is irrational to prejudge individuals. Each individual, whatever that person's physical characteristics, has unique strengths and weaknesses. Individuals cannot be prejudged.

Although legal and moral campaigns have been waged for many years against discrimination in the United States and Canada, many people continue to suffer from prejudicial acts. Times are slowly changing for the better, but the challenge is still there for company officers to assure that everyone in their company is treated equally regardless of their sex, race, or religious beliefs.

Discrimination against ethnic minority groups occurs along the lines of national origin or religion. It is safe to say that almost every ethnic minority group has been discriminated against at some time in U.S. history, although some have been more severely discriminated against and for a longer time. Blacks and Native Americans have especially suffered. Prejudice against an ethnic group is most likely to be evident in a geographic region when that group composes a minority of the region's population.

Any group that is identifiable as distinct in some way from a given population and constitutes less than half of the population is a minority liable to discrimination. The bigot always feels safer in persecuting members of a group who are fewer in number than the bigot's own group. Minorities are also sometimes subject to the tyranny of the majority.

Some women have been discriminated against as if they were a minority. With the entry of more women into the fire service, their acceptance within the ranks may become a concern for the fire officer similar to acceptance of other minorities.

The question has often been asked: "Must belonging to an in-group automatically imply hostility toward some corresponding out-group?" The answer is no. A family being an in-group implies that all other families in the neighborhood are out-groups, but hostility between families is not automatic. Hostility toward an out-group might draw members of an in-group closer together, but it is not psychologically necessary. Individuals can feel close to the members of their own family without hating or even disliking members of someone else's family.

The company officer must work diligently to eliminate discrimination within the company. To begin, the company officer must realistically examine personal feelings toward members of out-groups, both those already in the fire service and out-group members who might apply for entry. Next, the fire officer must constantly be aware of every word and deed that might be construed as unfair or discriminatory toward anyone with whom the officer deals.

SUMMARY

A group is defined as two or more persons who interact with regard to a common goal. Groups may be formal or informal. The elements of a group are a common binding interest, a vital group image, a sense of continuity, a set of moral values, and recognizing different roles within the group. All groups have role expectations. In the fire service, management defines these roles. Groups also have rules and regulations. Individuals within a group have certain needs that they are striving to meet. These needs as defined by Abraham Maslow are basic physiological needs, safety and security, belongingness and social activity, esteem and status, and self-actualization and fulfillment. As the basic needs are met, the person can aspire to meet the higher needs.

Transactional analysis is a method of analyzing human behavior. Socioeconomic factors, such as wealth, education, and occupation, may also have an influence on individuals within a group. Discrimination is a result of socioeconomic factors. With additional minorities entering the fire service, officers must ensure that existing discrimination is minimized; furthermore, it is the *responsibility* of company officers, as leaders, to set the example of nondiscriminatory attitude and totally eliminate discrimination of the personnel under their command. The result of this disposition is a fire company that operates smoothly and efficiently. The International Fire Service Training Association firmly believes that all human beings are equal, and that people can treat each other equally and with respect.

SUPPLEMENTAL READINGS

Drucker, Peter F. *Management: Tasks, Responsibilities, Practices.* New York: Harper & Row, 1974.

Effective Supervisory Practices. 2nd ed. Washington D.C.: International City Management Association, 1984.

Hersey, Paul, and Kenneth H. Blanchard. *Management of Organizational Behavior: Utilizing Human Resources.* 4th ed. Englewood Cliffs: Prentice-Hall, 1982.

Hitt, Michael A., R. Dennis Middlemist, and Robert L. Mathis. *Management: Concepts and Effective Practice.* St. Paul, Minn.: West Publishing Co., 1983.

5

Leadership As A Group Influence

LESSON OBJECTIVES

After completing this chapter and related *Student Guide* applications, company officer candidates should be able to:

- Recognize the three theories of leadership.

- Distinguish among leadership styles.

- Describe the key dimensions that determine the quality of an individual's leadership ability.

- Recognize the types of power used by leaders.

- Evaluate their leadership style and potential.

- Demonstrate the ability to organize and lead a group session.

This chapter addresses NFPA 1021,
Standard for Fire Officer Professional Qualifications (1987):

2-2.1	3-2.1
2-2.2	3-2.2
2-2.4	3-2.3
2-2.5	

Chapter 5
Leadership As A Group Influence

One of the roles that most firefighters expect company officers to fulfill is that of formal group leader. With the possible exception of the informal group, the formal group leader has a greater effect on the company than does any other factor. Often, a leader attempts to depend on one style of leadership, which is an acceptable approach in static situations. The fire service, however, is far from static. Situations in the fire service change more dramatically than in almost any other profession. Therefore, a company officer will be hard pressed to adopt one style of leadership that serves well in all situations. The officer must learn to recognize the need for different leadership approaches and the factors that justify their use. The officer must then learn to apply the different approaches at the point where they appear most appropriate.

Many company officers recognize and react to the demands placed on them as leaders without ever knowing that a particular leadership style exists. Much of leadership is determined by common sense. Many officers have learned to lead by example. Unfortunately, such on-the-job training has flaws. For example, these new leaders tend to repeat the mistakes of their leaders; furthermore, they fail to employ valid techniques their leaders did not use. This section will build upon the leadership common sense that is already possessed by most individuals.

THE BASIC VIEWS OF LEADERSHIP

In his book, *The Human Side of Enterprise,* Dr. Douglas McGregor contrasted two attitudes toward leadership-management styles, which he called Theory X and Theory Y. Each theory describes the attitudes supervisors hold about people, their needs, and their motivations.

Theory X

McGregor contends that supervisors develop leadership styles corresponding to one of these two views. The first type of leader, the Theory X leader, basically believes:

- The average worker is inherently lazy, dislikes work, and will avoid it by any means.

- Because of their inherent dislike of work, most workers must be coerced or directed to perform adequately by threats and punishment.

- The average worker prefers to be directed and shuns responsibility because of a general lack of ambition.

Theory Y

The second type of leader, the Theory Y leader, believes that:

- The average worker does not inherently dislike work—in fact, workers feel work can be as natural as play or rest.

- Workers will perform adequately with self-direction and self-control without threats of coercion.

- Workers will subscribe to organizational objectives if they associate those objectives with direct rewards.

- The average worker learns not only to accept responsibility, but in fact learns to seek responsibility.

- Only a small part of the worker's intelligence, ingenuity, and imagination is ever harnessed, and that under proper leadership workers will excel.

Theory X and Theory Y represent the extremes, and obviously the leader does not have to subscribe to one or the other. Both theories have worked well in the fire service under the proper conditions.

Leaders usually fall into two broad groups: those who have a concern for production and those who have a concern for people. A Theory X person would probably be most concerned with production, believing that:

- Workers are not inherently motivated to work; therefore, they have to be closely directed.

- Emphasis should be placed on production, because otherwise work would not be done; the worker is not self-motivated (Figures 5.1 a and b).

A Theory Y person would probably be most concerned with people and believe that:

- Workers, unless adversely depressed by leadership, will be motivated toward production just because of their inherent human drive (Figures 5.2 a and b on next page).

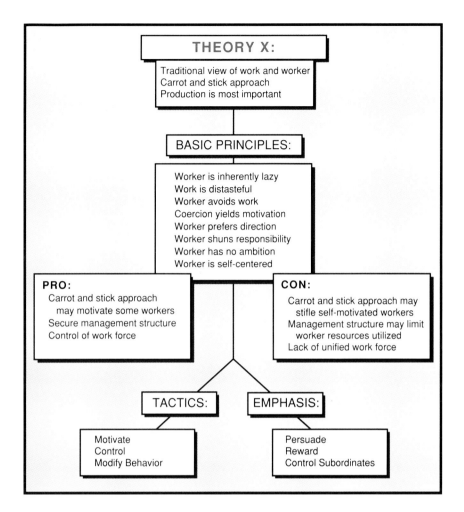

Figure 5.1a An overview of Theory X.

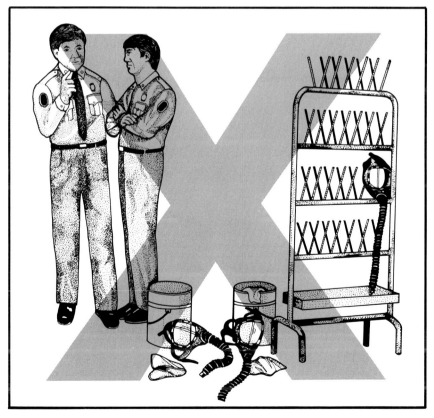

Figure 5.1b The Theory X manager contends that the worker is inherently lazy, avoids work, and must be supervised closely if anything is to get done.

● Workers will automatically push production to the upper limits when their needs are satisfied.

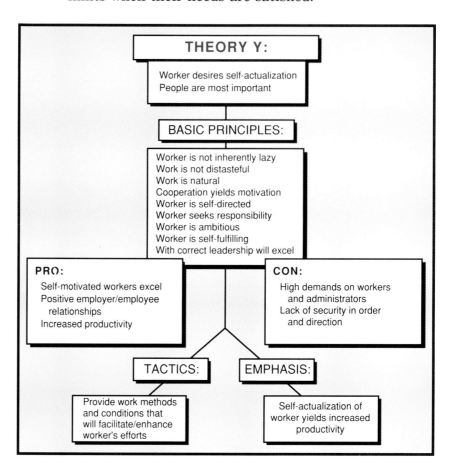

Figure 5.2a An overview of Theory Y.

Figure 5.2b The Theory Y manager contends that the worker is self-motivated and enjoys work.

Theory Z

In the early 1980s, William Ouchi coined the term "Theory Z Management." He has spent years researching Japanese companies and examining American companies using Theory Z management styles. The basic principle behind Theory Z management emphasizes that involved workers are the key to increased productivity. The Theory Z philosophy focuses the Japanese belief that each worker can perform autonomously (without supervision) because all workers are trusted. Japanese firms receive a high level of commitment and production from their work forces under the Theory Z management philosophy. The basic concepts include:

- Management style that focuses on the people.
- Employees remain with the company for life.
- Close relationship between work and social life.
- Workers' goal to produce economic success nurtures togetherness.
- Participative approach to decision making.

Theory Z principles definitely pertain to the fire service. Fire service operations are based on personal involvement, strategic and tactical teamwork, and all work for the good of the service (Figures 5.3 a and b on next page). Fire department members rely on trust and unity to conclude incidents safely, swiftly, and successfully. Firefighters also spend a great deal of time together. The result is a type of family relationship. This inevitable bonding promotes the goal orientation and direction that creates and induces the attitude "for the good of the service." A strong company officer recognizes and encourages this natural cohesion.

One of the major problems encountered with Z management theory is resistance to change. Once a pattern or method has been established for the performance of certain tasks, it is difficult to deviate from the technique. Similarly, new innovations or equipment are difficult to incorporate into the operation. These problems can be overcome by maintaining a progressive attitude and an open mind.

Real life concern for production and for people can exist simultaneously. McGregor's Theory X and Theory Y system fails except when directed toward specific individuals. Theory Z fails if the individuals under supervision do not exhibit the total unity and loyalty necessary—the attitude. One of the key points to remember when applying management theory to real situations is that a mix of different percentages from each theory is realistic. Basically, it is the *attitude* of the individuals that must be evaluated. Then, and only then, can the company officer select and mix a management and leadership style appropriate for the department and its individual members.

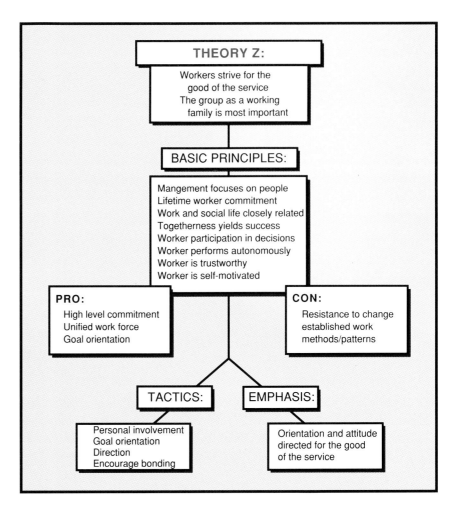

Figure 5.3a An overview of Theory Z.

THEORY Z:

Workers strive for the good of the service
The group as a working family is most important

BASIC PRINCIPLES:

Mangement focuses on people
Lifetime worker commitment
Work and social life closely related
Togetherness yields success
Worker participation in decisions
Worker performs autonomously
Worker is trustworthy
Worker is self-motivated

PRO:

High level commitment
Unified work force
Goal orientation

CON:

Resistance to change established work methods/patterns

TACTICS:

Personal involvement
Goal orientation
Direction
Encourage bonding

EMPHASIS:

Orientation and attitude directed for the good of the service

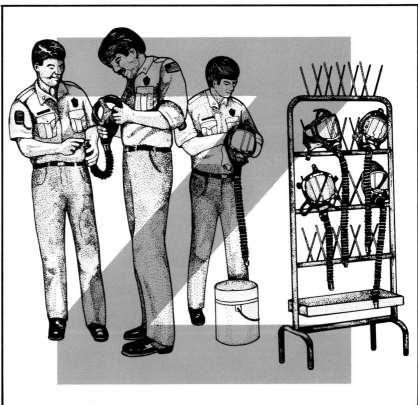

Figure 5.3b The Theory Z manager contends that the employer and the workers form a close working and social relationship.

The fact that all concerns exist simultaneously (with variations) indicates that a complete range of leadership attitudes can be derived. There are four basic leadership styles: bureaucratic leadership, single-issue leadership, middle-of-the-road leadership, and dual-issue leadership (Figure 5.4).

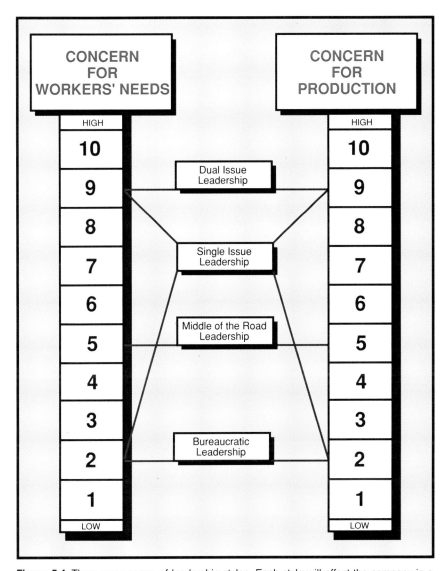

Figure 5.4 There are a range of leadership styles. Each style will affect the company in a different way and be appropriate at a different time.

Bureaucratic Leadership

Bureaucratic leadership is characterized by a low concern for production and low concern for people. This style of management generates just enough production to maintain the status quo. Typically, bureaucratic leadership exists in large organizations that are highly political and/or have extensive merit systems or labor contracts. However, small organizations are not immune to this type of management technique.

The bureaucratic style of leadership can produce strong social ties. It typically centers around job security and a certain camaraderie that evolves. Members of the group may lack social stimulation in some respects, but the security is pervasive. Individuals in such situations often make statements such as "I am willing to put up with the system because someday I will be in charge." This strong social atmosphere is also instrumental in maintaining the low levels of production. Group pressure discourages individuals who rock the boat by attempting to overachieve. Although a bureaucratic style of leadership may support the fulfillment of social needs, it squelches attempts of workers to meet most job-oriented self-esteem needs and higher level needs.

This blocking may be a result of the leader's insistence that workers not exercise initiative. Initiative would expose the supervisor's lack of concern for production. For persons attempting to achieve self-esteem through their job, the bureaucratic style can be frustrating. Highly motivated individuals usually do not remain employed in such organizations for long. When they do, they typically fulfill their needs through outside organizations such as civic or church groups.

Single-Issue Leadership

Single-issue leadership is characterized by an overriding concern for either production or worker needs. While single-issue leadership produces two vastly different sets of working conditions, the result is often the same: the moderately motivated workers leave for jobs that can better fulfill their need for self-esteem.

One form of single-issue leadership results from a high concern for production and a low concern for employee needs. This form is often associated with the Theory X perspective, attempting to arrange conditions so the human element only minimally affects production.

This form of single-issue leadership does not typically fulfill the workers' needs for self-esteem or self-realization unless the workers can take pride in the quality of their work. Pride in work comes when workers are allowed to exercise some initiative, and this usually does not happen under this authoritarian form of leadership. With the emphasis on production, it is unlikely that the workers' social needs will be filled. Such an authoritarian form of management tends to develop high turnover rates that reinforce the manager's Theory X concepts. Individuals with a moderate degree of motivation do not remain employed for long in such an environment before they find more appropriate work. The remaining employees typically stay only because other employment is not available, and in this situation act according to the manager's expectations. This form of leadership usually breeds discontent among the workers unless they recognize the work situation demands such a leadership style and they accept it.

The second form of single-issue leadership shows high concern for people and low concern for production. This relationship, which produces a comfortable, friendly atmosphere for workers, is a good representation of the Theory Y approach to management. The concern to meet the needs of the workers is high; theoretically, the workers will produce out of inherent drive, but this does not always happen. Because the manager lacks concern for production, the self-esteem needs of the workers may not be met, and the possibility of self-realization will be slim. The moderately motivated worker will not remain satisfied for long in this atmosphere. Most people expect to be involved in production in exchange for their wages. People tend to take pride in their work. In this form of single-issue leadership, the concern for production is low and the opportunity for taking pride in one's work is not frequent. Moderately motivated individuals do not tend to do well with such leadership.

Middle-Of-The-Road Leadership

Middle-of-the-road leadership has a moderate concern for production and a moderate concern for people. This style may seem to have advantages over the first two styles of leadership; however, it may be less preferable. Production under a middle-of-the-road style may sporadically exceed the amount of concern for production because the worker can show initiative, but this will not be the usual situation. Although the middle-of-the-road style is a way for a supervisor to "get by," it is certainly not the optimum. There are times when one or the other of the single-issue leadership styles may be advantageous, but the middle-of-the-road only provides mediocrity.

Dual-Issue Leadership

Dual-issue leadership couples a high degree of concern for people with a high concern for production. This style offers workers the luxury of working for a leader who is concerned about their needs and willing to allow them to produce. Under this style of leadership, most of the workers' needs, including self-realization, are attainable.

Dual-issue leadership implies worker commitment, which typically develops from the situation itself. If it does not, the leader must strive to show the workers how production goals reinforce their personal goals. When this is accomplished, workers will typically form a commitment.

Although there is a place on the fireground for the single-issue style of leadership, the dual-issue style is the most productive.

These four basic styles of leadership are all used in various degrees by fire service company officers. No one style can be utilized in all situations. When and with whom to employ each style is something a company officer must learn.

SIZING UP LEADERSHIP STYLES

The four basic leadership styles have strengths and weaknesses, and almost all have a place within the fire service. As there are Theory X, Y, and Z management styles, there are also Theory X, Y, and Z workers. Every manager has stories of employee X who was beyond motivation. These managers claim that employee X typified the Theory X concept. Those same managers also have stories of employee Y who was the perfect employee. The point is that factors beyond the officer's control determine which leadership style should be used. Moreover, the demand on leadership style will not remain constant. Even in the same situation, leadership styles will vary from individual to individual. There are three factors to consider when selecting leadership styles: the personality of the officer; the personality of the firefighter; and the situation.

The company officer should begin indexing personal factors long before promotion. The officer should have an accurate picture of personal motivation, strengths, weaknesses, expertise, and resources. As the company officer works with the firefighters, an attempt must be made to make an inventory of the personal factors.

- What are the individual's talents?
- What are the individual's weaknesses?
- What motivates the individual?
- How mature is the individual?

The officer who knows the answers can select an appropriate leadership style, matching the style with the characteristics of the individual and the situation.

DIMENSIONS OF LEADERSHIP

Company officers hold positions with a relatively high ability to influence other firefighters. With this ability comes a responsibility to use power effectively and to know how to influence others.

There are five key dimensions which determine the quality of an individual's leadership ability. An effective leader is one who can:

- Make other people feel strong, and help them feel they can influence their future and their environment.
- Build others' trust in the leader.
- Structure cooperative rather than competitive relationships.

- Resolve conflicts by confronting issues together rather than by avoiding or forcing a particular solution.

- Stimulate and promote goal-oriented thinking and behavior.

Making People Feel Strong

An effective officer makes other people feel strong. The officer helps people gain the ability to influence their future and their environment. When people feel strong, they enjoy their work, feel personally involved, and are motivated to continue and improve their work. Persons who feel strong try to be aware of their surroundings. They feel they are able to direct their lives and want to gain as much information about life's potential as possible. An ineffective officer makes other people feel weak. When individuals feel weak, they do not believe they control their fate. They work only when others tell them to work. Weak individuals feel no sense of pride in occupational accomplishments.

Consider a situation involving two officers and two companies. One officer made the firefighters working in the station feel weak, and the other officer made the firefighters feel strong. The first officer felt he had to know what was happening in all aspects of the company at all times. He insisted that all firefighters file weekly reports of operations. Decisions concerning personnel and changes in operating procedures had to have his approval. Any problems were supposed to be brought to his attention immediately. The second officer had monthly meetings with the firefighters in his station. He asked them to take part in setting the overall goals for the company. He wanted them to obtain his approval only for major changes in operating procedures and gave them most of the responsibility for their jobs. He told them to feel free to ask for his help on any matter.

The firefighters working for the first officer did what they were told because the officer used reward and coercive power to influence them. The officer used legitimate power to remind them they could be punished if they did not follow instructions. The officer treated them as if they were weak, and they felt weak in their organization.

The firefighters working for the second officer had control over what they did. They eagerly accepted responsibility for their activities. The supervisor based most of his influence on expert power as an expert in administration and in the different types of fire service operations. The officer asked to be considered a resource for help. By setting goals with the firefighters and maintaining a warm, friendly attitude, the officer based this influence on identification power rather than depending on the reward and coercive power that was a part of the position. The firefighters in the station felt strong and enjoyed their work.

The performance records of the two stations were similar, but the firefighters' level of job satisfaction was different. The first station had a high rate of transfers. A sense of urgency in the organization caused tension. The officer imposed an attitude of "hurry up and do the work, or else" in the station. The firefighters in the second station were satisfied with their work. They felt a personal challenge that made them work diligently and creatively. They had a tendency to treat each other in the same honest and friendly manner as the company officer treated them.

When a fire officer bases influence primarily on the ability to reward or punish a firefighter, a climate develops in which control of evaluations and the dispensation of rewards is the major motivational force. When firefighters are dependent on their officer for all recognition of accomplishment or quality work, they feel powerless. Officers who explain how they judge quality work to their subordinates and conduct evaluation discussion sessions with their employees are helping their firefighters feel responsible for their own work. The influence of the officer becomes based on shared values of quality work and self-appraisal, or expertise in evaluating the work, and as a result firefighters tend to feel strong.

Building Trust In The Leader

An effective leader makes subordinates feel they are a part of the organization and involved in the department's operations. If they have concern for each other as human beings and trust each other, they can work more efficiently for the group. The group needs their contributions to run effectively. Because the firefighters trust one another, they do not have to waste time worrying about what others are going to do to them.

Division Chief Allen was not concerned with building trust. He held regular meetings for the members of the division to discuss their work. Periodically he would meet with them to discuss their progress. There was little creativity in their solutions to problems. Interviews with several of the firefighters made it apparent that they were reluctant to come up with new ideas because they felt the officer would take the credit with top management. The firefighters did not trust the officer. They felt assignments were handled in a purely political manner. They thought Allen's major occupational goal was "to get ahead in this department."

Allen was fighting a battle with other divisions for funding. He wanted to expand the research staff, pay higher salaries, and attempt several new projects. In dealing with his subordinates, he tried to show his concern for the quality of their work and their job satisfaction, but something was missing. The subordinates responded to the officer's requests only because he could punish or reward them. Although he believed it was important to be an effective manager, he had not based his influence on types of power that would inspire trust. The firefighters did not feel a part of the division and were not aware of the goals. Therefore, the firefighters suspected the chief of using the group to satisfy his own needs.

What could he have done to build the necessary trust and commitment to the division? Had the chief clarified the goals of the division and explained how the group could contribute to the goals of the department, the firefighters could have seen how his actions related to their common goals, not just his personal goals. By sharing the proceedings of management meetings he attended, he could have highlighted for the firefighters the obstacles the division faced. Being more open would have led to increased trust. The officer's influence would have been based on identification and expert power rather than reward and coercive power: identification power because the firefighters would have felt he was concerned about them as individuals, and expert power because he would allow them to see he had special abilities as an administrator by discussing department goals with them.

Cooperating To Achieve Common Goals

An effective leader structures the relationship among firefighters so that they cooperate to achieve the shared goals of the company and cooperate with other companies to achieve the fire department's goal. In competition, one party usually wins and one loses. But even winners lose if they lose the trust or respect of their competitors. An effective officer will have firefighters work with each other to accomplish the department's objectives rather than against each other to accomplish their own objectives. People working together are more able to accomplish their personal goals than when operating alone.

An officer who creates competition among firefighters to build incentive runs a high risk. By structuring the situation so one person wins and others lose, one firefighter's incentive to work has increased slightly (at least during the competition), but it might slacken by the time the victory is won and the others have lost incentive. The results may represent an aggregate loss of incentive.

The officer's basic influence is based in part on legitimate power in the organization. If one tends to structure competitive relationships within the department, this legitimate influence tends to depend upon rewards (winning) and punishment (losing). On the other hand, if the officer structures cooperative relationships, the subordinates will depend less on the rewards of cooperation, and the officer can establish influence on a more effective combination of powers—legitimate power and expert power.

Confronting Conflicts Instead Of Running Away

An effective leader handles conflict by confronting it with subordinates. An officer should not avoid a problem by denying it exists, by forcing a solution without consulting the individuals involved, or by smoothing over the problem. A problem cannot be solved by running away from it.

One morning, the chief in charge of fire prevention and training received a call from a captain in the public education section. The captain said the training academy had not met a deadline for promoting a new program, and the officer over the academy admitted that the program would not be ready for Fire Prevention Week. The chief asked the captain to be in his office at one o'clock that afternoon. The chief stated that the issue could be settled then. The chief also called the officer from training and several other officers involved and asked them to attend. The meeting started with heated words between the officers, each blaming someone else for the delay. The chief quieted everyone by saying there were two goals for the meeting: first, they had to decide what should be done to maintain good public education; second, they would discover what caused the delay and correct procedures so it would not happen again. The chief stressed they were at the meeting to correct errors, not fix blame and punish someone for a mistake.

The questions concerning what to do next were quickly settled. As they discussed what caused the delay, people moved to the edge of their seats, ready to defend past actions. The chief asked for a historical rundown on how the new program and the production schedule developed. As each point was made, the chief was careful to check if it was challenged. If someone disagreed, the chief asked the group to arrive at a consensus on what really happened. Although the meeting took three hours, the officers began to work together. By mutually confronting different views of what had occurred, they arrived at an accurate picture. They found the delay was caused in part because some divisions wasted time complaining about other divisions instead of getting out the work. Once these disagreements were faced openly, the officers could understand each other's position and come to an agreement.

The chief, in this case, based initial ability to influence the officers on expert power as an administrator, although he also used legitimate power as the executive of the division to call the meeting. Once the meeting began, the chief moved beyond relying on legitimate power to influence the process of the meeting by emphasizing that the purpose of the meeting was to correct the situation, not to fix blame or punish people. In other words, the chief did the unexpected; he eliminated the use of reward or coercive power in the meeting to open the way for the expert authority to dominate.

GOAL ORIENTED THINKING

The development and implementation of specific goals and objectives have long been positive management tools in modern fire service activities. A goal is defined as "the end toward which effort is directed." The key to goal oriented thinking is proper communications. It is important that all individuals involved are working from the same "road map" if the end for which the organization is working is to be achieved. Joint identification of the goal and continual discussion and evaluation will keep all concerned parties exerting the needed *effort* to maintain a goal directed thought process.

POWER STRUCTURES

Power is one person's ability to influence another. For instance, a person may be given advice, offered a job, or threatened with a pay cut; however, a more subtle form of influence uses the person's reaction to the leader to initiate control. Two psychologists, John French and Bertram Raven, have identified five types of power:

- Reward power
- Coercive power
- Identification power
- Expert power
- Legitimate power

Think about the words and images associated with power—words like dictator or force; images like war or riots; words and images with bad connotations. *Power* itself is not bad. The goals of power may be "good" or "bad," but the exercise of it is neither. Yet the use of power can be judged; it can be effective or ineffective. When people react to power as something "bad," they are usually saying that either the use of power is ineffective, or the goals of power are questionable. The effectiveness of power, specifically power in a work-organization setting, is discussed in this section.

Reward Power

Reward power is based on one person's perception of another's ability to grant rewards. It increases in direct proportion to the amount of rewards a person sees another as controlling. Within an organization, giving someone a raise or bonus, promoting one to a job with more responsibility, or expanding one's budget are all highly visible uses of reward power to influence a person to do a better job. Stopping by someone's work place just to say good morning is a more indirect use. Results will depend on the perception of the leader's ability to provide an apparently tangible reward.

Coercive Power

Coercive power is based on one person's perception of another's ability to punish. The strength of coercive power is proportional not necessarily to the ability to punish but to the employee's perception of the ability to punish. Where the perception is faulty, some tension is likely until perception and reality are in closer accord. A reprimand for not submitting a report on time, scorn for mistakes, the denial of a raise or promotion—these are examples of coercive power used to force performance of job activities closer to the stated standards. Withholding a promised or standard reward is also a use of coercive power.

Identification Power

Identification power follows from one's perception of the similarity between one and another, or the desire to be like another. The Horatio Alger stories and Mickey Rooney-Andy Hardy series influenced American youths to work hard. These models influenced youths because of identification power; many youths had the same economically poor childhood, possibly were even tempted to break the law. Leaders who are respected and well liked derive their power from many sources, but their identification power should not be underplayed. Many people are willing to be influenced by people who they feel are friends and can be trusted at a personal level.

Expert Power

The total "amount" of knowledge in the world is continually increasing because of technological and communication advances. The increase is important, but just as important is the individual's growing awareness of the resulting complexities in the social and physical environments. As knowledge increases, new forms of relationships develop and individuals become more interdependent. Thus, members of society look for leaders who have a broad base of knowledge, leaders who have the ability to apply their knowledge to solve problems. Expert power is based, then, on one person's perception that a leader's expertise, knowledge, and approach can help the individual better adapt to a complex world.

Legitimate Power

Legitimate power stems from three sources: shared values, acceptance of a social structure, or the sanction of a legitimizing agent. In a fire company, an officer assigns work to firefighters. They do the work because they accept the management structure of the company which makes it legitimate for the officer to assign work.

SUMMARY

Company officers influence the company because they are the formal group leaders. The company officer should study different styles of leadership and be able to use them in the many different situations that the company is placed in. There are three basic views of leadership: Theory X, Theory Y, and Theory Z. The Theory X leader believes that workers are lazy, dislike work, and must be constantly supervised and directed. The Theory Y leader believes that workers enjoy work and that workers can work with minimal supervision and direction. The Theory Z leader believes that each worker can perform without supervision because they are trusted and committed to each other and their work.

There are four basic styles of leadership: bureaucratic leadership, single-issue leadership, middle-of-the-road leadership, and dual-issue leadership. The company officer must learn when and with whom to employ each style. There are five dimensions that determine the quality of an individual's leadership ability. They are making people feel strong, building others' trust, cooperating, confronting conflicts, and promoting goal oriented thinking.

Power is one person's ability to influence others. The five types of power are reward power, coercive power, identification power, expert power, and legitimate power. If company officers work to understand the different styles and dimensions of leadership, and when to use the different types of power, they will be doing the utmost to use their formal leadership abilities to influence the company.

SUPPLEMENTAL READINGS

Effective Supervisory Practices. 2nd ed. Washington D.C.: International City Management Association, 1984.

Gratz, David B. *Fire Department Management: Scope and Method.* Beverly Hills: Glencoe Press, 1972.

Hersey, Paul, and Kenneth H. Blanchard. *Management of Organizational Behavior: Utilizing Human Resources.* 4th ed. Englewood Cliffs: Prentice-Hall, 1982.

Hitt, Michael A., R. Dennis Middlemist, and Robert L. Mathis. *Management: Concepts and Effective Practice.* St. Paul, Minn.: West Publishing Co., 1983.

Management in the Fire Service. Didactic Systems, Inc. Boston: National Fire Protection Association, 1977.

Ouchi, William. *Theory Z: How American Business Can Meet the Japanese Challenge.* Reading, Mass.: Addison-Wesley, 1981.

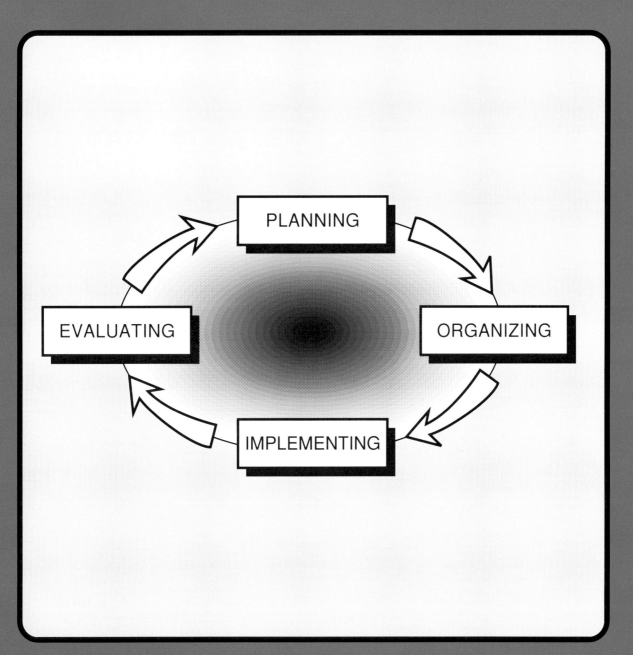

PLANNING

ORGANIZING

IMPLEMENTING

EVALUATING

6

Elements Of Management

LESSON OBJECTIVES

After completing this chapter and related *Student Guide* applications, company officer candidates should be able to:

- Recall the definition of *management.*

- Explain the management cycle.

- Describe the major resources available to the company officer for planning and organizing.

- Match to their correct descriptions steps used in the management-by-objectives system.

- Explain the importance of employee evaluation.

- Recognize the major areas of goal setting at the company level.

- Demonstrate the ability to use the MBO system to write management objectives.

- Demonstrate the ability to use the MBO system to evaluate employee performance.

This chapter addresses NFPA 1021,
Standard for Fire Officer Professional Qualifications (1987):
3-7.1
3-7.2.

Chapter 6

Elements Of Management

Management has been defined in numerous ways by many experts on human resources. Managers have been compared to orchestra leaders, football coaches, and traffic officers. Harold Mace, Executive Director of the International Fire Service Training Association, has been overheard saying that on most work days he feels like a juggler, attempting to keep "as many balls in the air" as possible at one time (Figure 6.1).

Actually, company officers as middle managers are required to establish and maintain a routine for company members that can reach major proportions. Management has been defined as "the art of accomplishing organizational objectives through and with people."

THE MANAGEMENT CYCLE

In order to manage personnel and other important resources in a fire company, an officer must have a plan of action. Individuals in the company must be aware of the plan. Open communication is important. Chief Alan Brunacini

Figure 6.1 Managing a fire company requires juggling many activities in a specific period of time.

of the Phoenix Fire Department lists five things firefighters want their supervisors to do:

- Tell me what you want.
- Train me to do it.
- Give me the tools.
- Get out of my way.
- Tell me how I did.

These five basic thoughts closely parallel the management cycle (Figure 6.2):

- Planning
- Organization
- Implementation
- Evaluation

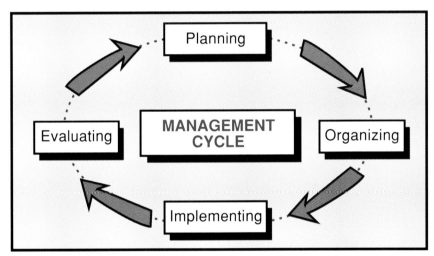

Figure 6.2 The management cycle is the order of tasks that managers follow to ensure effective operations.

PLANNING

Planning is the first step in any type of management. It is impossible for a manager to tell someone what to do if the manager has not already made that decision. The manager must have a plan. There are three types of management planning: long range, medium range, and short term.

Long-range plans typically extend several years and sometimes cover as long as 20 years. Because of the role the company officer plays within the department, the company officer typically does not become involved in long-term planning. This type of planning is generally completed by fire department administrators.

Medium-range plans cover from one to five years. The company officer is generally involved in providing information for medium-range planning, usually when fire department administrators ask company officers to evaluate the capabilities of their companies. However, most medium-range planning is still performed at higher levels than that of the company officer.

The company officer is most likely involved in short-term planning, which typically deals specifically with assigning personnel to attain immediate goals or meet day-to-day demands. Short-term plans, which in some cases may cover up to a year, allocate resources to achieve or maintain elements of medium- or long-range plans.

Achieving short-term goals implies three things:

- The company officer must know the medium- and long-range goals of the department.

- The company officer must know the capabilities of the members of the company.

- The company officer must set goals and/or develop a plan for the company.

The company officer must also remember to include proper maintenance of facilities and equipment in company planning. Even though space is limited by building walls and property lines, available space must be analyzed to determine its best possible use.

Fire department equipment represents a substantial investment. Company officers must see that it is used to the department's best advantage. Officers must first appraise the equipment and determine if better or different equipment is needed. They should observe the equipment in use and ask firefighters if the equipment serves their purposes well. Because money for new equipment is not always available, equipment must be maintained and replaced when obsolete or beyond repair. By making higher management aware of equipment needs, company officers demonstrate they are on top of their jobs even though all requests may not be approved.

Company officers must monitor the plan closely so supplies are used appropriately and not wasted. Even though individual items may cost little, wasted supplies add up to sizable amounts over time. The company officer must remind firefighters that conserving supplies is in their interest. Money spent on wasted supplies cannot be used to raise wages or improve working conditions. Although all waste cannot be eliminated, conservation can significantly reduce wasted resources.

BUDGETING

Budgets and the budgeting process serve as planning and informational tools to help fire administrators and their departments decide what emphasis they want to give to certain areas.

The process also informs chief officers, city administrators, elected officials, and the public (which provides a good portion of the funding), how the department is being run.

Putting together a preliminary company budget helps chief officers decide the kinds of program improvements and cutbacks they can implement in the upcoming year. It also gives them a better grasp on the kinds of long-term changes they need to make. Taking the company's budgets into account while hammering together a budget proposal for the department helps chief officers decide how the department should fit into the overall job of running the city. Approving the final document in the glare of the public arena forces elected officials to back up policy decisions with hard cash after citizens have had a chance to express their opinions.

The Budgetary Process

When putting together a preliminary budget for the upcoming fiscal year, preferably with input from company personnel, company officers will often start with budgets from earlier years. They will check to see how accurate they were and how relevant previous expenditures are for the current situation. Unneeded expenses can be cut and new needs included.

The preliminary company budget goes to the chief administrators of the department. This early proposal might go back and forth between the company officer and the administration several times, with several compromised versions, before all preliminary budgets are put into a proposed budget package for city officials to consider. Company officers might be called on to explain and justify their proposals in budget sessions before department administrators adopt the budget. The department administrators will then compose a preliminary department budget and present it to the city administrators for review. The entire process then repeats itself between the department administrators and the city administrators.

Describing the process is simple, but getting what the company needs in a time of fiscal restraint takes savvy. Noted fire service author David B. Gratz has listed several methods company officers can use to justify their preliminary budgets:

- Try to identify fixed, recurring expenses. Once officials are convinced the expenditures will come up regularly, they will not be in controversy when the department budget comes up for approval in following years. Such fixed expenses include vehicle maintenance, building maintenance, tools, office supplies, cleaning supplies, and miscellaneous services.

- Let officials know how spending funds in a certain program now will bring savings in the future.

- Use what has happened in the past to justify more spending in a problem area. Be prepared to back up all such requests with hard, reliable data from the company's record-keeping system.

- Compare the company's operations and situation with those of other companies or divisions in the department. Be sure to use this approach with other tactics because department officials are usually resistant to this line of reasoning by itself.

- Miss no opportunity to impress department officials with your managerial abilities. Be able to operate efficiently with less. Demonstrating a sincere desire to cut costs without cutting services can go a long way toward making the company's preliminary budget request more palatable.

There are other methods that department heads have used to justify their budget requests, but Gratz advises not to use them because of their questionable professionalism. The following are some of the ones he lists:

- Placing unneeded items in the budget so administrators and elected officials can find them and, with much public self-righteousness, cut them out. Behind this tactic is the assumption that the preliminary budget will be cut regardless, so the company officer might as well inflate it and get the department what it needs. Company officers who can justify their requests can often get what they want if the city has no higher priorities.

- Inflating costs in one program so the company officer can later transfer the excess to another program that had less of a chance of being approved at the desired level.

- Using the emotional parade-of-horrors technique, claiming that if administrators fail to give the company officer what the company needs, the city faces sure destruction.

Budgetary Controls

Once the company's budget is adopted, the company officer can expect the budget office to monitor company expenditures with a variety of controls that can be classified as traditional or behavioral. The traditional types are used and sometimes abused. The behavioral types are considered more effective.

Traditional budget controls include the following techniques:

- Line-item accounting, where every expenditure is deducted from the amount remaining in the account. This method usually puts a burden on overspending, and the controls on spending are usually vested in the budget office.

- Budgetary accounting reports, usually monthly or quarterly, showing how much has been spent for what and how much is left in each account.

- Percentage deviation reports that show the percentage of allocations already spent compared to what "normally" should have been spent during the time period. This control operates on the erroneous assumption that if the fiscal year is, for example, one-third over, no more than one-third of the allocation has been spent.

- Allotments that split up the allocation into quarterly or monthly segments and allow department heads to spend no more than that during the allotment period without having difficult times with the budget office.

- Position controls, usually required because most city departments spend a majority, up to 95 percent, of their funds on personal services. This control limits the number of positions, thus the number of employees, and consequently the amount of money that can be spent on this major budget item.

- Purchase order and contract award review that requires department heads to get approval from a purchasing office and perhaps from a central budget office before buying budget-authorized items. With this system, there is a possibility that purchases approved when the budget was adopted can be turned down when the company officer tries to spend the money.

- Travel and subsistence clampdowns.

- Training dues and subscription limitations.

Among behavioral controls:

- Motivation often provided by letting more people have a say in setting priorities and seeing that they are met.

- Management by objectives, which helps people understand why they do what they do and generally causes them to work more efficiently and cooperatively. This commitment grows from the fact that they have had a hand in setting the goals and objectives of the organization.

ORGANIZING

After the plan is developed, the next step in the management cycle is organization, which is allocating specific resources to meet the needs of the plan. There are four basic resources available to the company officer: human resources, physical facilities, training, and time.

Human Resources

Human resources include the skills and capabilities of the members of the company and of persons working in other agencies providing services to the company officer. These agencies include other divisions of the fire department, such as fire prevention, training, and personnel services; other governmental agencies such as city administration, federal and state agencies, schools, and colleges; and organizations such as the firefighters' unions and service organizations.

The company officer should consider these resources during organization to increase the effects of company efforts on and off the fireground. Begin by recognizing and developing the skills and capabilities of company members, and add to these from outside sources.

Physical Facilities

Physical facilities include buildings, equipment, and supplies that the officer must match with details of the plan. The difference between planning and organizing resources is illustrated in the following example. In planning a new company inspection program, the company officer decided to include a classroom lecture by someone from fire prevention. During the organization stage, the company officer asked a specific person, Dick Green from fire prevention, to speak and reserved classroom A-2 at the Training Academy from 2:30 p.m. until 3:50 p.m. on May 19.

When organizing resources to increase the effects of the plan, the officer must remember that communities also offer many physical facilities for fire company use. The company officer should compile a list of all the services available from the community.

Training

Training is an important resource that can be used to enhance other resources. The company officer is the primary trainer of company members, but other training resources are available—the fire department training division, local schools and colleges, and state and federal fire training programs. During organization, the company officer must attempt to match the right training content with the demands of the plan to increase the plan's potential.

Time

The company officer's time is a resource that must be carefully planned. Some officers are always complaining about not having enough time while others seem to keep on top of things. All company officers have the same amount of time available—24 hours a day. What matters is using time productively. When there are more tasks than time allows, the company officer must set priorities and organize tasks so that as much gets done as possible. When appropriate, the company officer may need to delegate authority to others to get the job done.

Each day before starting work, the company officer should make a list of all the items that must be completed that day—shift meetings, training exercises, station and vehicle maintenance, and others. Next, the company officer should place all the items on the list in order of priority. The company officer should remember that emergencies take priority over other situations, making it difficult to set up a definite time schedule.

When setting up a time schedule, the company officer must remember that an average of 70 percent of administrative time is spent dealing with regular job assignments—handling emergencies, training personnel, and managing the company (Figure 6.3). Regular job assignments will rank high on the fire officer's list of priorities.

Figure 6.3 Most of an officer's time is spent doing regular job assignments. For this reason it is very important that the officer plans time effectively.

Finally, the fire officer's time schedule may include special assignments, the unexpected tasks that crop up during the day. Many experts feel that a supervisor should spend no more than 10 to 15 percent of the time dealing with special assignments unless upper management gives them top priority.

The desk calendar is one of the simplest scheduling tools to use. Schedule events as far in advance as practical, noting events automatically as they are due. Emergencies will disrupt the schedule, so leave enough extra time for flexibility.

Urgency is an important criterion to consider when ordering tasks. As a task deadline approaches, the urgency for completing the task increases. An essential task that must be completed soon acquires a high priority. Successful supervisors usually concentrate on activities that give the greatest potential return to the organization for the time they spend. Forecasting potential return is not always easy to do, but fire officers should try to think in terms of investing time and the returns their investment will bring.

The supervisor must also plan the firefighters' time. In planning work schedules, officers can assume that most firefighters will do a fair day's work, but they will not work all day at top speed. Allow for fatigue and periods of rest and relaxation. Plan for employee absences, such as regular days off, holidays, and vacations, to ensure the department functions smoothly.

When the fire officer must deal with routine assignments, such as station and vehicle maintenance, it may help to delegate some authority to another member of the company (Figure 6.4). Through proper delegation, an officer can decrease the workload until only 10 percent of an officer's time is spent dealing with routine work assignments.

Delegating authority is an important way to gain extra time. Company officers who refuse to delegate authority exaggerate their own importance, and in effect refuse to admit that a firefighter could handle many of their tasks. By delegating authority for certain activities, company officers increase their importance to the department by gaining time to devote to more important

Figure 6.4 An officer can increase the time available to handle special tasks through effective delegation.

tasks, reducing the distraction of relatively unimportant tasks. Delegating is obviously necessary when the supervisor is faced with more work than can be done in a specific time, but it can be used wisely even during periods of relative inactivity. Firefighters get accustomed to having specific work assignments, and the officer must know that there are individuals who can be trusted with part of the workload. Delegation also helps develop the capabilities of future officers.

It is important to note that the company officer is a supervisor as well as a firefighter. At the fire scene, the company officer spends the most time directing firefighters, reporting to the officer in command, and assisting in fire fighting operations as necessary. Effective time management calls for the manager or supervisor to remember the distinction between occupational and managerial duties.

The art of organizing then becomes a matter of matching specific resources with the demands of the plan. Asking some basic questions will assist in this evaluation: (Figure 6.5)

- Have personnel safety problems been identified?
- Does the amount of human resources available meet the demands of the plan? If not, where can more be obtained? Who specifically is going to do what?
- Is the equipment available to meet the plan? If not, where can it be obtained? Can other equipment be used instead?
- Are the personnel involved trained to do the job? Are they trained to use the equipment?
- How much time is needed to complete the task? Is there enough time available? How can available time be increased?

When the company officer has answered these questions (and others that may arise) and matched resources with goals, the task has been organized.

IMPLEMENTING

Once the plan is established and the resources organized, the next management step is implementing the plan, which often is easier said than done. Implementation begins by telling the firefighters about the plan, including:

- The objective
- The action that is going to be taken
- The personnel involved
- The task or job to be done
- The equipment that is to be used
- The time available

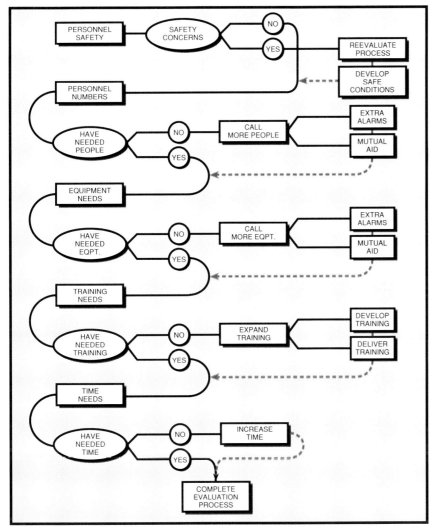

Figure 6.5 Organization involves coordinating specific resources with the demands of the plan.

Then the firefighters should be set to work, and the company officer begins phase two of implementation. During the work, any shortcomings in the officer's plan will become obvious. As the company officer recognizes mistakes in the plan, they must be corrected. The officer must also make sure the members of the company are following the plan. The company officer's main tasks during phase two of implementation are directing and controlling.

Directing

Directing or leading is the most important of the company officer's leadership functions. It involves supervising firefighters as they fight fires or perform other tasks.

The first officer to arrive at a fire assumes the fire chief's or district chief's authority and directs the operation until a superior officer arrives. All fire officers should know the pre-incident plans and standard operating procedures, how to size up the situation, and adapt the pre-incident plan to the situation. Non-fire fighting responsibilities may also be delegated to the company officer. Changing command from company officer to superior is not so critical during nonemergency operations because circumstances do not change as quickly.

While directing firefighters, the company officer acts as a manager, an instructor, and a coordinator, often at the same time. Mature judgment and the ability to make quick decisions are important when directing in dangerous situations.

When directing a fire company in public, the company officers must make sure the crew projects a good image. Public opinion is critical and is usually based on the way firefighters conduct themselves.

Controlling

Remember that controlling involves seeing that organizational objectives are met as planned and taking corrective action if necessary.

The company officer, as a first-line supervisor, controls in many instances by observing. The company officer works directly with firefighters more hours per day than first-line supervisors in most other occupations; therefore, the officer is in a position to recognize problems in meeting department objectives before higher management does. Controlling also requires an officer to keep superiors informed, even when things are not going well. The officer must resist the temptation to hold back bad news from higher management.

Controlling company operations is typically a short-term objective. The company officer controls operations on a day-to-day, monthly, or six-month basis depending on what the objectives call for. Control standards and time frames are set up with objectives when a management by objectives system or something similar is used. Controlling by using progress evaluations and time frames is further discussed in the section on management by objectives.

EVALUATING

The last phase of the management cycle is evaluating the operation, which should be done soon after the operation ends (Figure 6.6). Often the company officer will just review the operation and make mental notes. At other times, the whole company should be assembled and the operation discussed. The major question to address is, "What can we change to improve our operation?"

Evaluation should not be used to lay blame. When it is, it will fail for two basic reasons:

- Individual comments will be defensive instead of constructive.

- Operations are a series of decisions, and assessing blame focuses only on the poor decisions instead of evaluating both the good and bad decisions.

The facts or suggestions that come out of evaluation should be incorporated into the planning phase of the management cycle (Figure 6.7).

Figure 6.6 Every fireground operation should be evaluated to determine what was done right and what was done wrong.

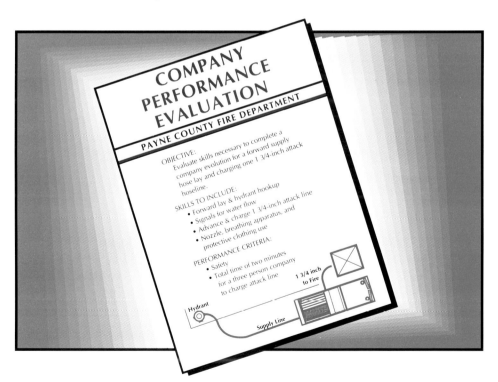

Figure 6.7 Evaluations identify inconsistencies or errors and provide a recourse that can improve future responses.

GOAL-SETTING PROCESS

Management is responsible for setting organizational goals and making them known to employees. If goals are not set for them firefighters will set their own goals, which may not coincide with those of management. Firefighter goals will likely be aimed at personal gain, and the organization ends up being used as a method to attain personal goals. In such situations, many firefighters may view organizational policies and procedures as inconveniences. This is a rather negative but convincing reason for organizations to set goals if management is to achieve what it requires.

In the fire service, the fire chief or chief executive officer of the fire department, assistant chiefs, and other primary officers have responsibility to develop department policy. Department policy is the basis for developing procedures to be followed by department employees. Policymakers must keep an eye on these procedures to see if they are practical. The company officer is responsible for informing higher management of progress toward organizational goals and management must encourage such communication. Through proper control, higher management can make necessary adjustments in department goals and plans.

Planning for the fire department starts with setting organizational goals. These goals should be challenging to employees as well as desirable to management. Departmental goals should be clearly set down in definite, measurable objectives that are realistic and attainable (Figure 6.8). The goal-setting process involves commitment of department personnel, clear thinking, and good forecasting.

LONG-RANGE PLANS AND GOALS

Planning for extended periods of time, up to 20 years, is long-range planning. These plans and goals attempt in a general way to anticipate how the fire department will best serve the community. However, specific costs are practically impossible to predict so far into the future. Long-range plans show that the department is looking forward even though these plans may require many adjustments.

The National Fire Codes published by the National Fire Protection Association call for the fire chief to project goals for 5-, 10-, and 20-year periods, including budget requests. As time goes on, changing conditions will indicate the need for adjustments in plans and goals.

MEDIUM-RANGE PLANS AND GOALS

Goals to be reached over one year are called medium-range goals. Medium-range plans reflect reasonable projections of departmental and community needs for that period of time. For

Figure 6.8 Goals and objectives must be realistic to be attainable.

example, community growth might indicate the need for a new fire station and, accordingly, appropriate planning can be done even if the exact site is unknown.

SHORT-RANGE PLANS AND GOALS

Goals scheduled to be reached in less than a year are called short-range goals. These are planned in greater detail than long- or medium-range plans.

IMMEDIATE PLANS AND OBJECTIVES

Immediate plans and objectives were probably once short-, medium-, or long-range plans and objectives. As plans grow more detailed and their completion grows nearer, they move from their original category to a category less remote. Finally, after possibly many changes, they are scheduled for immediate action. Of course, some plans are put into effect soon after their inception. Placing plans and goals into immediate, short-, medium-, and long-range categories helps keep department priorities straight.

Immediate plans and objectives have highest priority, at least for those involved in carrying out the immediate objective program. Programs like these in particular need regular and frequent review to ensure that the objectives are being met.

MANAGEMENT BY OBJECTIVES SYSTEM

Management by objectives is a leadership tool that makes planning work and evaluating results easier. Everyone in management, from the fire chief to the company officer, works within a personal span of supervision toward attaining clearly spelled out objectives. Management by objectives enables fire department supervisors to measure results objectively. *Objectives are originally chosen with measurability in mind so that objective appraisal is simplified.* A standard performance may be set, or employees may be allowed to use their own methods to achieve results. A definite time limit should also be set.

Progress must be checked at specified intervals. Objectives that turn out to be unrealistic may then be altered. Reaching specific objectives at the fire company level furthers objectives at the next higher level in the department.

Most management experts hold that employees should participate in setting the objectives they are expected to attain. Disagreements arise over the appropriate level of participation within the organizational structure. Helping to set objectives is meaningful only if firefighters are sincere in helping to establish realistic and challenging objectives. But participation in setting objectives is recommended because the satisfaction it brings helps motivate firefighters. An effectively operating management by objectives system creates a climate for motivation while moving toward organizational goals (Figure 6.9).

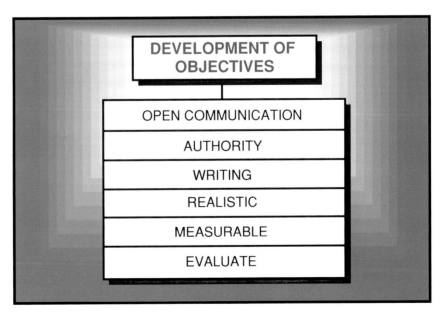

Figure 6.9 Objectives are identified and initiated to attain goals.

Five steps to remember in using management by objectives are:

Step 1: Objectives must be recorded in writing.

Step 2: Objectives must be realistic, attainable, and measurable.

Step 3: Lines of communication must be open, upward and downward.

Step 4: Authority and responsibility must be spelled out for each person involved.

Step 5: An evaluation chart or form must be developed to answer the question, "How are we doing?"

SETTING OBJECTIVES IN THE MANAGEMENT BY OBJECTIVES PROCESS

Objectives to be met by each fire company must be in harmony with overall department goals. Under a management by objectives system, objectives are set by fire officers and firefighters working together. Chief officers can help coordinate a management by objectives system, but company officers, as first-line supervisors, are responsible for involving as many firefighters in the system as possible. The degree of participation allowed firefighters depends on how far the company officer trusts them to come up with realistic and challenging objectives. In practice, firefighters usually set objectives higher than company officers might expect. The firefighter who sets personal objectives with the officer's encouragement, or firefighters who meet with the company officer to set group objectives, will probably be more committed to the objectives than if they have not participated in the process. Of course, the company officer must have certain objectives in mind when meeting with individual firefighters or the company. Having ideas about how department goals can be reached by company activities is part of the company officer's planning responsibility.

The process of mutually setting objectives requires regular performance appraisal or evaluation of results after plans for reaching objectives are put into effect. The company officer sits down with each firefighter and asks what progress is being made toward the objectives. The fact that objectives were set up to be measurable makes appraisal easier. Much of the evaluation is shared by the officer and firefighter, making a generally difficult job easier for the company officer.

SUMMARY

The company officer should understand the elements of the management cycles. They are planning, organizing, implementing, and evaluating. Planning at the company level mainly involves evaluating short-term goals. One type of short-term goal is a budget. In budgeting, the company officer plans company expenses for the next year. Organizing involves allocating specific resources to meet the needs of the plan. The four resources available to the company officer are human resources, physical facilities, training, and time. Implementing the plan involves directing and controlling. Directing is the most important leadership function of the company officer. Controlling is seeing that the objectives of the plan are met and, if necessary, taking corrective action. As soon as the plan is carried out, it should be evaluated. Evaluation involves reviewing the operation and determining what, if any, action should be taken to improve things in the future. Management by objectives is a tool that can help the company officer organize responsibilities. Objectives and a clear time line are set. The results of a plan are easier to obtain this way. A good management by objective program involves regular performance appraisal and evaluation of the results after the objectives are met.

SUPPLEMENTAL READINGS

Effective Supervisory Practices. 2nd ed. Washington D.C.: International City Management Association, 1984.

Fire Protection Handbook. 15th ed. Quincy: National Fire Protection Association, 1981.

Gratz, David B. *Fire Department Management: Scope and Method*. Beverly Hills: Glencoe Press, 1972.

Hicks, Herbert G., and C. Ray Gullett. *Management*. 4th ed. New York: McGraw-Hill, 1981.

Management in the Fire Service. Didactic Systems, Inc. Boston: National Fire Protection Association, 1977.

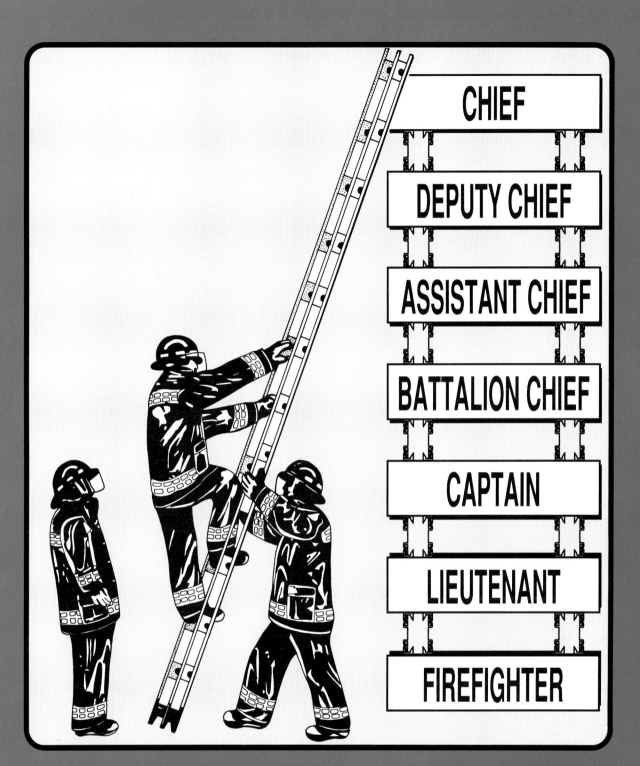

CHIEF

DEPUTY CHIEF

ASSISTANT CHIEF

BATTALION CHIEF

CAPTAIN

LIEUTENANT

FIREFIGHTER

7

Company Motivation

LESSON OBJECTIVES

After completing this chapter and related *Student Guide* applications, company officer candidates should be able to:

- Recall the definition of *motivation*.

- Recognize the factors that influence an individual's behavior.

- Explain how influencing factors may be used to motivate firefighters.

- Recall the affective needs of most individuals.

- Explain how an individual's affective needs may be used to motivate firefighters.

This chapter addresses NFPA 1021,
Standard for Fire Officer Professional Qualifications (1987):
3-2.1
3-2.3.

Chapter 7
Company Motivation

Ralph Waldo Emerson is credited with the statement, "Our chief want in life is someone who will make us do what we can." In today's fire service, effectiveness as a company officer is measured not only by what the officer accomplishes, but also by what the firefighters under his or her supervision accomplish. The overall role of managing a fire company requires skill in planning, organizing, motivating, controlling, and innovating. The ability to motivate is a key skill for a supervisor.

Motivation can be defined as the amount of physical and mental energy that a person is willing to invest in a particular activity or project. Actually, we can say that to motivate means to move. Fire officers managing companies are concerned with the direction of that movement because individuals can be motivated negatively as well as positively. Former President Dwight Eisenhower was credited with the statement, "Leadership is the ability to get a person to do what you want them to do, when you want it done, in a way you want it done, because they want to do it." Motivation is already within an individual's capability. The task of company officers is to know how to generate higher levels of motivation in individuals under their supervision.

The company officer's responsibility for motivating company members is shared with higher management. The company officer has little or no control over such factors as wages, labor relations, and major policy strategies. Nonetheless, these policies do influence the motivational climate in which a company officer and individual members of that company work. The company officer does control such factors as developing and demonstrating an attitude of dedication to the department's goals and objectives. These are factors that the company officer alone controls through daily contact, and they affect an individual firefighter's ability to give his or her best.

The administration has an obligation to provide safe working conditions; establish standards of performance; set rules, regulations, and standard operating procedures; and, in career departments, provide for stable employment and fair wages. Above that base, company officers continue to fashion the environment in which company members function.

Developing and demonstrating an attitude of dedication to the department's goals and objectives is a major responsibility for the company officer. When firefighters first enter the fire service, their attitudes are chiefly influenced by the company officer to whom they are assigned. With this in mind, the company officer should always try to instill an attitude of pride and responsibility in the firefighters. A firefighter who is motivated to maximum performance will be an asset not only to the company, but also to the entire department.

INDIVIDUAL BEHAVIOR

Behavior in a narrow sense consists of an individual's actions. But to understand behavior, one has to understand the four basic factors that influence an individual's behavior:

- The individual's moral and ethical beliefs
- The individual's perspective on life
- The individual's expectation of the situation
- The individual's specific needs

These four factors combine to guide the individual's choice of action, and the results can reinforce the individual's attitudes (Figure 7.1).

Figure 7.1 Four factors combine to influence the individual's actions. These factors can be used to guide the individual to meet department goals.

When behavior is viewed this way, the company officer can no longer attempt to deal with behavior just as actions. To change actions, the company officer must change the factors influencing those actions. The officer must alter the individual's moral and ethical values and the individual's perspective on life. Altering behavioral influences is often termed motivation. The company officer must remember that motivation may be positive, influencing actions to coincide with those expected by the officer, or may be negative, influencing actions to contradict those expected by the officer (Figure 7.2). Either type of motivation can result when individual influences change. The important task for the officer is to know the influences that positively motivate people.

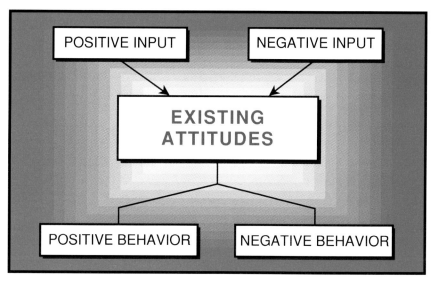

Figure 7.2 It must be remembered that although influencers can be used to motivate people positively, inappropriate actions can motivate people negatively.

AFFECTING MORAL AND ETHICAL INFLUENCES

Most people's moral and ethical beliefs are formulated and confirmed by the time they enter the fire service. To change such beliefs requires a substantial outside influence over a long period. Producing short-term motivation by affecting an individual's moral and ethical beliefs is restricted mostly to reinforcing existing beliefs.

Scott and Kevin had worked together for several years on the city fire department and had developed a close respect and friendship for each other. Scott had a family business as a second occupation and was considered open and honest in his dealings. Kevin had come from a background that included being raised in a strange family environment and being left alone much of the time to fend for himself. However, he has an exceptional work record and has never had problems with fire department rules and regulations. Both had worked hard at becoming professional firefighters and shared hopes of being promoted in the near future.

During one shift in late August, their engine company was dispatched to assist a rescue unit at a private swimming pool. The first company on the scene was Kevin and Scott's, where they found an apparent drowning victim. The victim was pulled from the pool by the landlord of the apartment complex and was lying on the pool deck. Kevin and Scott began cardiopulmonary resuscitation. They were later relieved by the members of the rescue unit.

Kevin and Scott were then requested to check the victim's apartment for any prescriptions that might belong to the victim. After being admitted to the apartment by the manager, the two firefighters were left alone in the apartment. Upon checking the rooms, they discovered some medication and a large sum of money.

Kevin immediately recognized the opportunity to steal the money, knowing that the victim would probably be unable to recall that the money had been left. There was also little chance of anyone else finding out that the money was missing. Scott sensed that it was wrong and that there could be problems if they stole the money (Figure 7.3).

Scott openly contested the idea of taking the money and explained that they were trusted by the victim and the department to carry out their duty as expected and not to take advantage of the situation. Kevin argued the "who would ever know" type arguments and then listened to Scott's point of view.

In the end, Kevin and Scott returned to the rescue squad with the information and left the money in the secured apartment. Scott had motivated Kevin not to do something wrong by explaining and reinforcing Kevin's existing beliefs.

AFFECTING PERSPECTIVES

People's perspectives include their views of themselves, the world, and other people. Perspective correlates with expectations, but perspective is the general view of all situations, while expectations are specific to a certain situation. Everyone has heard the old saying about the difference between an optimist and a pessimist: The pessimist says a glass of water is half empty, and the optimist says the glass is half full. Both recognize the same quantity of water, but the optimist feels a little bit better about it. The optimist has a different perspective.

The company officer can provide information that affects the firefighters' perspective, convincing them the glass is half full. Sometimes this can be done by arranging circumstances. If firefi-

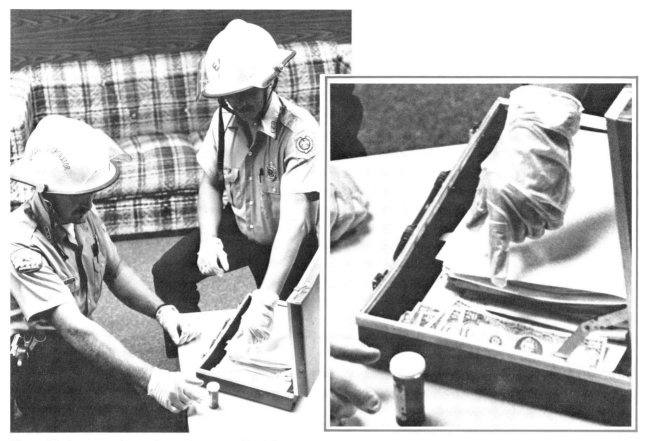

Figure 7.3 One person's morality can have a positive influence on another.

ghters have negative self-images, if they do not think of themselves as doers or accomplishers, they should be given tasks with high visibility and an above-average probability of success. Upon completion, firefighters should be reinforced by sincere praise and recognition. False praise can be quickly seen for what it is. The high visibility of the task will give other firefighters a chance to reinforce their colleagues. Some tasks that have a high visibility factor and a high probability of success are mopping and waxing a floor, taking care of the lawn, and organizing the library.

Of course, poorly motivated firefighters must be given other tasks, too. If possible, team insecure firefighters with those who seem to consistently do good work. This method usually helps both firefighters. One drawback is that insecure firefighters may let the others do all the work. The best insurance against this is to tactfully instruct the team that each member is to do an equal share of the work.

AFFECTING EXPECTATIONS

People react in situations with respect to their expectations of the outcome. For example, if a person is asked to burst a balloon with a pin, the person will begin to flinch before sticking the balloon in anticipation of the loud pop a balloon makes when it bursts. Knowing that people react to a situation with regard to their expectations of the results, the company officer can motivate firefighters by changing their expectations of the situation. Often this can be done simply by mentioning possible outcomes firefighters may not have fully considered.

Motivating by affecting expectations takes consistency. If a company officer makes it clear what actions will be taken if a certain situation arises, the firefighter will take that into consideration before acting (Figure 7.4). But the officer must follow through as promised. In addition, the officer should expect policy statements to be tested.

Figure 7.4 People react to situations based on their expectations.

Tom and Joe are captains on the same shift, but at different stations. In late December, a new facial hair policy was instituted to become effective January 1. This policy arose from the safety issue raised with facial hair preventing an adequate seal when using self-contained breathing apparatus. The policy stated that any individual who maintained facial hair would not be allowed to work in any capacity as a firefighter. It was up to the station captains to enforce the policy with their companies.

Both captains announced to their companies that they were required to enforce the policy and that anyone who did not comply would be sent home. The policy met with moderate resistance, but most firefighters recognized its necessity for safety reasons.

On the morning of January 2, both companies came to work and each had several firefighters who had not complied with the new policy. Tom arranged to have replacements brought in and sent the two men home. Joe, on the other hand, sat down with his two men who did not meet the new policy and had a stern discussion, but did not send the men home.

Six weeks had passed and Joe still had problems getting his firefighters to comply with the facial hair policy and with several other new policies. Tom experienced little or no trouble with his company. It is evident that Tom's company knew that if they did not comply with departmental policies, Tom would apply departmental disciplinary actions as needed. Joe's company members knew that Joe would not enforce the new policy and took advantage of that fact.

Tom's firefighters were motivated by his actions to comply with departmental policies while Joe's company members found little or no motivation to comply with a policy. Officers have the ability to alter or influence individual's expectations by demonstrating the consequences of certain behaviors. They should use that ability to manage and influence company members in order to accomplish departmental goals and expectations.

AFFECTING NEEDS

Personality differences account for much of the variation in individual behavior in fire departments. These differences are defined largely in terms of needs: for achievement, power, and affiliation. Many individuals bring different sets of needs to their work, and an officer cannot afford to overlook them. To motivate efficiently and effectively, a company officer must learn to assess human needs.

First, the officer must pay particular attention to the thoughts and feelings of the firefighters. How do the firefighters talk about their experiences? What seems to be on their minds when they are involved in a task? From what do they seem to get the most satisfaction? By asking these questions, the officer will learn the dominant needs of the firefighters. Everyday responses provide excellent keys.

Take, for example, a firefighter who seems to be motivated by a need to achieve. The firefighter talks about department goals and seems to gain more satisfaction from reaching these goals than from recognition. The firefighter likes to be considered a "planner" and is proud of the detail put into the plans the firefighter acts upon. Not only does this person enjoy the competitive nature of the work, but has told the chief several times that the freedom and responsibility of the job are important. All of these things indicate this firefighter needs achievement.

The officer should pay close attention to the behavior of different firefighters under different circumstances. Behavior is largely a function of aroused motivation, and the officer must watch the nature of the situation carefully. It would be foolish for an officer to think that a firefighter who behaves appropriately in a situation calling for achievement-oriented behavior is strongly motivated by achievement. With this warning, the officer can use the following list of key indicators to help determine needs.

Indicators Of High Achievement Needs For Firefighters
- Sticks with a task until completion
- Continually tries to get feedback on achievements
- Enjoys challenges
- Strives to accept responsibility

Indicators Of High Power Needs For Firefighters
- Likes to discuss controversial subjects
- Likes to be in charge
- Is status oriented
- Tries to find out who is in charge of each job assignment

Indicators Of High Affiliation Needs For Firefighters
- Does not like to work alone
- Tries hard to be friendly and to make friends
- Enjoys group projects
- Is sensitive to what others think

Although these statements are general, they typify some of the important behaviors that characterize the three needs. An officer should observe firefighters in several different situations to get a clear idea of individual needs.

ORGANIZATIONAL TASKS AS MOTIVATORS

Even if an officer knew what the firefighters' needs were, those needs would have to be matched with the demands of each organizational task to get the most out of each person. It might be a conflict of needs and situation to hire a young athlete to do clerical work. It is poor management to promote a power-motivated individual into a position where that individual will have to take orders rather than give them. If it is impractical to manipulate personnel, then the attributes of the tasks might be altered somewhat.

To motivate firefighters, the officer must consider the basic nature of the tasks to be performed. Different tasks require different kinds of worker behavior and different patterns of work motivation. For example, many tasks require taking risks and assuming individual responsibility. In these, achievement motivation seems especially important. Some routine tasks do not require this kind of motivation. Assembly lines are often most efficient when set up to afford the workers opportunities for interaction and affiliation motivation. Realizing that tasks can be matched with individuals gives the company officer strong leverage. The problem is to measure the motivational demands of various jobs in the organization.

The motivational demands of tasks can be measured with a task evaluation survey, using the following questions, and rating the answers by the following criteria.

- Rank tasks "high," "moderate," or "low" by the response to each of the 15 questions in the section that follows.

- Give a ranking of "high" 3 points, "moderate" 2 points, and "low" 1 point.

- Set standards of what constitutes a "high," "moderate," or "low" score for each question. For example, "high" for question #11 would be 8 to 10 people, "moderate" would be 3 to 8, and "low" less than 3.

- Realize that scores mean little. It is the relative score in each of the three groups that defines the motivational demands of the task.

Is It An Achievement Task?

1. How much latitude does a firefighter have to set the work pace and work methods?

2. How much choice does a firefighter have when it comes to getting help or direction from someone else?

3. To what degree does errorless and efficient performance contribute to company efficiency?

4. To what extent does the task challenge the abilities and skills of the firefighter?

5. Does the task provide clear, unambiguous feedback about the quality of performance?

Is It A Power Task?

6. How much opportunity does the firefighter have to direct co-workers?

7. How much time is available for interaction while working?

8. To what degree does the task require the firefighter to deal directly with fire department officials?

9. How much control does the firefighter have over procedures and policy?

10. To what degree will the firefighter be free from close supervision?

Is It An Affiliation Task?

11. How many people must the firefighter interact with every two hours?

12. How many people can the firefighter interact with in the work area?

13. How dependent is success upon the cooperation of other firefighters?

14. How much time is available for nontask interactions while working?

15. To what extent does the task allow maintenance of stable working relationships?

COMBINATION OF FACTORS AS A PRIME MOTIVATOR

Any method of affecting influences on behavior can have a short-term effect on a firefighter. But to have long-term, consistent motivation, the company officer must strive to affect as many of the influencing factors as possible. This requires time and study of the firefighters in the company, but will be well worth any investment the officer makes.

SUMMARY

Behavior can be thought of as the manner in which a person acts. There are four factors that influence an individual's behavior: moral and ethical beliefs, perspective on life, expectation of the situation, and specific needs. A person's behavior can be modified by changing the factors that influence that individual's behavior. Each individual in this society has varying degrees of need for achievement, need for power, and need for affiliation. To motivate a person to his or her maximum performance level, the company officer should assess the needs of that individual and assign tasks that will more fully satisfy those needs. If motivation is to be long-term and consistent, the company officer needs to affect as many behavior-influencing factors as possible. This takes time and effort, but will result in a motivated fire fighting team.

SUPPLEMENTAL READINGS

Effective Supervisory Practices. 2nd ed. Washington D.C.: International City Management Association, 1984.

Gratz, David B. *Fire Department Management: Scope and Method.* Beverly Hills: Glencoe Press, 1972.

Hersey, Paul, and Kenneth H. Blanchard. *Management of Organizational Behavior: Utilizing Human Resources.* 4th ed. Englewood Cliffs: Prentice-Hall, 1982.

Leadership In The Fire Service. 1st ed. Stillwater, Okla.: Fire Protection Publications, Oklahoma State University, 1967.

Management in the Fire Service. Didactic Systems, Inc. Boston: National Fire Protection Association, 1977.

8

Career Counseling

LESSON OBJECTIVES

After completing this chapter and related *Student Guide* applications, company officer candidates should be able to:

- Explain how employee evaluation serves both the interests of the department and the firefighter.

- Distinguish between formal and informal evaluations.

- Discuss the negative aspects of informal employee evaluation.

- Distinguish between local and national evaluation standards.

- Recall the phases of the evaluation cycle.

- Describe the actions possible under criterion evaluation.

- Recognize the steps in behavior modification.

- Recall the order of the steps in the progressive system of discipline.

- Demonstrate the ability to
  —Conduct an evaluation interview.
  —Apply the progressive system to properly discipline an employee.

This chapter addresses NFPA 1021,
Standard for Fire Officer Professional Qualifications (1987):

3-2.3	4-4.6
3-6.4	4-7.1
	4-7.3
	4-7.5
	4-7.7
	4-7.10.

Chapter 8
Career Counseling

A recruit arriving at the academy on the first day of a fire service career brings a host of skills. In fact, most of the recruit's personal skills, habits, aptitudes, and attitudes have already been instilled. The majority of the fire-related skills a firefighter needs, however, still must be developed (Figure 8.1a). In hiring the recruit, the fire department has entered into an implied partnership: The department will guide and train the individual, and the individual will work to become an asset to the department (Figure 8.1b).

8.1a The majority of a rookie's fire-related skills must be developed.

Figure 8.1b As firefighters are continually trained, they become an asset to the department and achieve self-satisfying goals.

The rate, degree, and magnitude of the fire-related skills the recruit develops are predominantly influenced by the skills and habits the recruit brings into the fire service. Whether these skills are fully realized as assets to the department depends on the attitudes and actions of the department. It is the obligation of the department to develop the individual's skills into a valuable resource. This obligation means that the individual must receive career counseling throughout his or her tenure.

The best interests of the organization and the individual will be served when the recruit continually develops in the fire service. As the department trains and aids the individual's development, the individual will improve and better serve the fire department.

EMPLOYEE EVALUATION

The most productive way to harness the individual's potential is to align the requirements of the organization with the aspirations and skills of the individual. The best way to monitor this alignment is with employee evaluation. The alignment is most often recognized in the formal evaluation session, although it continues throughout the cycle (Figure 8.2).

Figure 8.2 Evaluation is an excellent chance to provide direction for the good of the firefighter, as well as the good of the department.

The evaluation session is most often instituted by the department for the good of the individual, and implicitly for the good of the department. Unfortunately, employee evaluations have a negative connotation in some firefighters' minds, generated in part by improper evaluation techniques. Proper evaluation is just an objective examination of the relationship between the firefighter and the fire department. The primary purposes of evaluation are to determine how the firefighter is functioning relative to the needs of the department and to define how departmental requirements can be aligned with the firefighter's goals.

Evaluation should not be a judgment, negative criticism, or reprimand. The evaluation cannot be productive in a negative environment. In such instances, the department and the individual lose.

The Basis Of Employee Evaluation

Many departments consider employee evaluation a period of time set aside to formally counsel the employee. Often, it is only included in a firefighter's first year. Firefighter evaluation, however, should be an ongoing process. As a matter of fact, fire officers and fellow firefighters evaluate their colleagues every day. Perhaps the evaluation is not formal or even conscious, but it is a realistic part of fire department operation. However, this informal evaluation will seldom work toward aligning individual and department needs.

There are two reasons why "evaluation by personality" is not acceptable. First, the evaluation is subjective, based on the terms of the evaluator. In other words, the firefighter is judged by criteria developed by other firefighters based on their opinions, beliefs, and personalities, not by any accepted standard. Generally, it is impossible for the firefighter being evaluated to meet these subjective standards, especially when that firefighter does not even know what the standards are. Second, evaluation by personality does not allow the firefighter to participate in the evaluation. This type of evaluation is a negative factor in cultivating human resources.

The department faces a problem with informal employee evaluation or evaluation by personality because there is no method to curtail it. It is an ongoing process. The department can only ignore the problem and accept possible losses in personnel resources, or institute a formal evaluation program to align individual needs and department goals. Neither choice will eliminate personal subjectivity, but the formal evaluation can help negate the effects of personalities in management.

If formal evaluation is to nullify evaluation by personality, a set of criteria must be developed and implemented. Legally, employee evaluation must use job-related performance objectives as criteria. An employee can be evaluated only on ability to perform a job-related task and on the manner in which the task is performed day to day. The two tests are:

- Is the employee performing the job or task to acceptable standards?

- Is the employee performing the job or task in a manner compatible with the requirements of the job or task?

Fire Service Standards

When applying the employee evaluation criteria, officers must have a definition of reasonable standards. Obviously, every fire officer is not free to make up a personal set of standards. Many fire officers, however, do not know what standards are applicable.

In the fire service, there are two major sources of standards. The first and most important is the local jurisdiction. The local fire chief determines what the department standards will be.

This does not mean, however, that the local chief is free to arbitrarily set standards for the department. There are some broad and basic legal requirements:

- A standard cannot arbitrarily exclude a given segment of society from employment or advancement. The courts have declared that race, sex, height, and weight are invalid standard criteria.

- The standard must apply to the employee's ability to accomplish specific tasks required to properly perform the job.

- The standard must apply to the entire group doing a specific job.

The chief cannot use standards for evaluation that are more stringent for one firefighter than for another. This does not exclude the chief from requiring the department to receive training to raise its standards. It merely means that every firefighter performing in the same position in the department should be able to meet the same standards. Length of service, company location, or similar factors cannot influence the standard.

The second source of standards is a nationally recognized consensus of minimum skills needed for a given fire service position. The currently recognized standards are as follows: (Figure 8.3)

- National Fire Protection Association, *Standard for Fire Fighter Professional Qualifications, No. 1001.*

- National Fire Protection Association, *Standard for Fire Apparatus Driver/Operator Professional Qualifications,* No. 1002.

- National Fire Protection Association, *Standard for Professional Qualifications for Airport Fire Fighters,* No. 1003.

- National Fire Protection Association, *Standard for Fire Officer Professional Qualifications,* No. 1021.

- National Fire Protection Association, *Standard for Professional Qualifications for Fire Inspector,* No. 1031.

Figure 8.3 The National Fire Protection Association has published standards that are considered to be the minimal skills needed for fire service positions.

- National Fire Protection Association, *Standard for Professional Qualifications for Fire Investigator,* No. 1033.

- National Fire Protection Association, *Standard for Professional Qualifications for Public Fire Educator,* No. 1035.

- National Fire Protection Association, *Standard for Fire Service Instructor Professional Qualifications,* No. 1041.

- National Fire Protection Association, *Standard for Professional Competence of Responders to Hazardous Materials Incidents,* No. 472.

These standards provide guidelines for local departments to use in setting their goals. They provide a yardstick with which to measure the ability of local firefighters. The company officer should know what standard the department is using for firefighter evaluation and ensure that the firefighter has access to written copies and fully understands them. Caution must be exercised, however, to ensure that no one is required to meet the standard unless every individual doing that particular job is also required to meet it.

At a given department, written fire department policy states: "Effective August 1, 1979: New firefighters shall demonstrate donning the protective breathing apparatus within a 30-second time period while wearing full protective clothing before being eligible for pay increment one." Firefighters already receiving the pay increment were not affected.

Firefighter Jim Jones became eligible for pay increment one on September 15, 1979, but failed the donning requirement and did not receive the pay increase. He filed an appeal to the local civil service board stating that the requirement was discriminatory because all firefighters were not required to meet the same standard.

October 31, 1979, the board held that Jones had been wronged. They held that the standard was discriminatory because all other firefighters were not required to meet it, and Jones was granted the pay increment and back pay. The department altered the requirement to read: "Effective November 1, 1979: All firefighters shall demonstrate donning the protective breathing apparatus within a 30-second time period while wearing full protective clothing before being eligible for further pay increments."

Fire Chief Tom Johnson issued an order that all firefighters must pass a physical fitness test that included doing

10 push-ups and 25 sit-ups in 90 seconds, running a mile in 12 minutes, and hoisting a 50-pound weight 20 feet with a 1-inch diameter rope. Firefighters not passing the test were not eligible for promotion. Several firefighters failed the test and appealed their cases by questioning the validity of a required physical fitness test. During the hearing, the chief produced evidence that the test was copied in part from a nationally recognized standard. In addition, he demonstrated several job-related tasks that might require the firefighter to use the same muscles needed to perform the hoisting fitness test, which was not included in the standard. The chief said he used the test because it measured the ability of the firefighter to perform the job at a level specified as the department standard.

The appeal board ruled in favor of the chief. The board held that the tasks were recognized standards indicating the firefighter's ability to perform the job.

Compatibility Of Performance With Job Requirements

Compatibility of performance addresses the method an individual uses to perform particular tasks. There are conceivably several ways to meet a requirement or standard; however, some methods may not be acceptable. There are two major areas that may be examined to determine if the performance is acceptable: safety and employee working relationships.

In evaluating an employee's performance compatibility, two basic questions should be answered:

- Does the individual perform assigned tasks without taking unnecessary risks?

- Does the individual perform in a manner that does not undermine or disrupt the ability of the organization to function properly?

The fire service is one of the most hazardous occupations in North America. Not every task can or will be performed safely because firefighters cannot control their work environment. However, firefighters can take the responsibility to accept risks only when the situation warrants it. Unfortunately, there are no set rules, formulas, or scales to determine acceptable risk for every incident. For example, an act at one fire that earns a firefighter a commendation for heroism may, at a different fire, cause a suspension for recklessness—or worse, the firefighter's life (Figures 8.4a and b). The decision to discipline is the company officer's prerogative. Each fire has different criteria and interpretations.

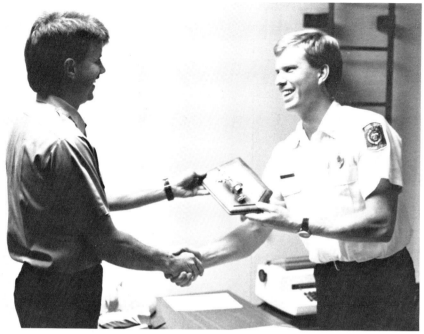

Figure 8.4a Acts of heroism during an incident can result in the firefighter receiving a commendation.

Figure 8.4b An attempt at heroism at an incident may be recklessness and cost the firefighter his/her life.

With so many possibilities, evaluating employees on safety seems impossible, but it is not. The firefighter who takes unnecessary risks at a fire will often perform daily tasks haphazardly or unsafely. By examining the everyday work habits of the firefighter, the company officer can get a good idea whether a firefighter tends to work safely or takes unnecessary risks.

The second criterion—compatibility—is easier to analyze. Actions that tend to undermine the ability of the organization are often easily spotted. These problems are caused by people who do their assigned tasks in a way that disrupts the effectiveness of the organization. They may, and often do, perform their tasks adequately, but because of other actions, they tend to cause disciplinary problems or dissatisfaction within the group. For example, Carol Brown was an excellent firefighter with a good career ahead of her. She worked hard and did everything well, except that she was a teaser. Brown never missed a chance to chide someone. Her quick wit often made it amusing, but sometimes caused hard feelings. Her actions bred dissatisfaction within the company.

When using this evaluation criterion, specific examples and instances must be cited. Otherwise, the matter simply becomes the company officer's word against the employee's.

THE EVALUATION CYCLE

As with any operation, employee evaluation follows a perpetual sequence. This means the last step of the sequence ties into the first step. The evaluation cycle has five phases: interaction, dialogue, behavior reinforcement, behavior modification, and criteria evaluation (Figure 8.5).

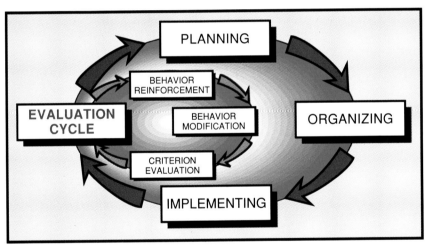

Figure 8.5 The evaluation cycle is an important part of the overall department management cycle.

Interaction

The success of a department ultimately depends on how the individuals of the organization interact while handling their tasks. Information for employee evaluation comes from examining this interaction.

While supervising a company, the officer must examine how each firefighter interacts while performing assigned duties, living with other members of the company, and meeting obligations to the department. The officer can then analyze if the firefighter is conforming to expectations. The officer can also assess how the department is fulfilling the firefighter's expectations.

Dialogue

If employee evaluations examine the implied partnership between department and firefighters, then each side must voice its requirements for serving the partnership. The company officer voices the requirements of the department, and the firefighter must voice his or her requirements. Further, the company officer must listen for the department.

The dialogue phase is most often associated with the formal evaluation session, but the dialogue is continual. Most company operations result from dialogue, although this dialogue does not mean the firefighter has a voice in every decision made. Through dialogue, the firefighter does provide important feedback to the company officer in most situations.

During the formal evaluation, the need for dialogue is most acute and often most difficult. The company officer must confer with the firefighter and explain how the individual is meeting the standards accepted by the organization. The firefighter has a chance to have input into the partnership. There are few other methods that allow the individual and the organization to coordinate their needs as effectively. Most departments leave space on the evaluation form for firefighter comments and require the individual to sign the form. This gives the firefighter a chance to express views about how the partnership can best use his or her talents to meet the needs of the organization. Both partners can also evaluate what changes will tend to lessen the individual's weaknesses.

Behavior Reinforcement

During the reinforcement phase, the department rewards the firefighter for trying to fulfill their mutual needs. The first step in rewarding the firefighter's positive actions is to recognize which actions or traits of the individual are truly positive. It is usually easy to recognize firefighters who work well in the organization, but it takes a reasonable amount of examination to determine which specific actions of the firefighter are responsible.

Recognizing an individual's strengths is a good reinforcer of positive action.

When an individual realizes that one's performance is recognized as a positive factor, that individual will be more likely to continue performing positively. To reinforce positive behavior, the company officer should incorporate all the motivators possible into the company operation. This reinforcement logically begins in the evaluation phase.

The organization benefits in a second way if the evaluation procedure recognizes the strengths of the firefighter. Often, when a specific skill is required to complete a special department project, fire department administrators can review evaluation reports to determine if the special skill has been reported. The department may be able to draw upon that skill source instead of hiring or training someone new.

> Company Officer John Davis had noted that firefighter Bill Green doodled and sketched during his idle time. The station officers decided to redesign the station bulletin board. They concluded that some type of cartoon character might enhance the appearance. They decided on a drawing of a beaver, the local college mascot. Capt. Davis contacted Green about drawing the mascot. Green agreed and did an outstanding job. Capt. Davis noted Green's talent on his next evaluation.
>
> About six months later, Capt. Davis received a visit from Deputy Chief Terri Smith of training. Smith told Davis that she needed an artist to help complete a new training manual, but had been unable to hire one because it was a part-time position. Smith asked Davis about the notation on Green's last evaluation. Davis told her about Green and showed her the mascot Green had drawn.
>
> The two officers spoke with Green about the situation. Green said he was interested. After a short period, Green was assigned temporarily to the training division. The manual turned out well, and Green received a special citation for his work. Green eventually was assigned permanently to the training division as an artist.

Behavior Modification

While it is easier in employee evaluation to describe a firefighter's good behavior, it is also necessary to describe unsatisfactory behavior. Evaluation should let firefighters know where they stand with respect to the needs and requirements of the organization. To praise the satisfactory and neglect the unsatisfactory will not meet the needs of the department.

It is as incorrect to examine only the good points as it is to examine only the bad points. In these situations, the firefighter will have some idea of standing, but will not really be sure which direction to work. Evaluation of only satisfactory points or unsatisfactory points is like giving the firefighter an address without a street name. The firefighter will end up with only a vague idea of where he or she is going.

Behavior modification is a three-step process. The first step is to recognize and define unsatisfactory behavior; the second is to make the firefighter aware of specific acceptable standards; and the third is to define a course of action that must be followed to correct unsatisfactory behavior.

DEFINING UNSATISFACTORY BEHAVIOR

The problem must be recognized and defined precisely. It is not adequate or fair to tell the firefighter that his or her conduct is unsatisfactory unless the firefighter can be told why. Generalities and vagueness must be avoided. The employee must be told the exact problem.

> Company Officer Thomas noted that Firefighter McDonald consistently did not wear his hair according to fire department requirements. Officer Thomas reported the offense on McDonald's next evaluation report and gave McDonald a weak rating because of his unsatisfactory appearance. McDonald worked hard during the next quarter to shine his shoes, press his uniform, and polish his brass before each shift. On the next quarter's evaluation, Thomas again cited McDonald for unsatisfactory appearance. McDonald was confused and confronted Thomas, asking what was wrong. Thomas told McDonald that his uniform always looked good, but that he needed a haircut.

SPELLING OUT THE STANDARD

Explain to the firefighter the specific acceptable standard. Behavior and attitudes are subjective; everyone has a slightly different perspective or opinion. The reason departments have developed written standards is to eliminate this range of perspectives. The standard should define the objective in terms that cannot be misinterpreted.

When unsatisfactory behavior is noted and the firefighter is informed, he or she must be made aware of standard requirements. It is unfair to assume that the firefighter knows the standard. The purpose of the evaluation is to point out when the firefighter is or is not complying with standards, and the standards should be shown to the firefighter and explained.

Three major issues can be cleared up in the firefighter's mind by providing the standard. First, the firefighter's behavior is shown to be unsatisfactory in comparison with the standard. Little doubt should remain that the behavior needs modification. Second, the amount of correction required can be precisely determined. The firefighter knows how much improvement is necessary. Third, the firefighter is shown that the correction is a part of departmental policy and not a personal attack. If the standard is vague or leaves doubt in the firefighter's mind, the officer should advise the firefighter that the issue will be examined by the next higher officer in the chain of command. The three should meet to resolve the difference. If this is not possible, the higher officer's interpretation should be in writing.

CORRECTING UNSATISFACTORY BEHAVIOR

The company officer is obligated to define a course of action correcting the unsatisfactory behavior. Remember, the basic objective of the evaluation is to align the behavior of the firefighter with the needs of the organization while using the firefighter's resources to the maximum. When the firefighter performs unsatisfactorily, it is not because the individual is not trying, but because that person needs additional skill development or direction.

In defining the plan of action, the officer should make every effort to let the firefighter define a personal plan. A Theory Y management technique works best in these instances. The officer should define the outside limits and prompt the firefighter to develop a plan. For this reason, it may not always be possible to develop the plan during the formal evaluation session. It is acceptable to meet with the firefighter after one or two shifts, but it must be made clear that a plan must be developed at that time.

When the firefighter develops the plan, he or she will be more likely to follow through with it. Developing a plan will also build a sense of security in the firefighter. The company officer, however, must take care to guide the firefighter away from pitfalls. The company officer should counsel the firefighter who attempts to do more than is possible by coming up with a plan that does not provide the necessary training or that requires unavailable resources. In accepting the plan, the officer must remind the firefighter that it is a joint venture between the department and the firefighter.

The evaluation process should define how the firefighter can attain the necessary additional skills. This definition should include whether the firefighter must learn a new skill or refresh an old skill. In addition, the following information must be provided:

- What the standard is
- How the training will be provided
- What level of proficiency is expected
- What timetable will be met
- What resources are required and available
- What will happen if a change is not made

Criteria Evaluation

Inevitably, some evaluations will bring the department to an impasse with the firefighter. A point will come when the firefighter's behavior cannot be made compatible with the requirements of the department (Figure 8.6). At this point, the

Figure 8.6 The firefighter must be allowed to speak during the evaluation while the company officer listens.

company officer, acting for the department, should request a criteria evaluation. The department may determine that the standard is indeed inappropriate. If this is the case, the standard should either be revised or discarded.

DISCIPLINE

If the criteria evaluation determines that the standard is appropriate and fair, the next step is to discipline the firefighter who is performing unsatisfactorily. If discipline is used, progressive steps should be used. The progressive system of discipline is as follows:

Step 1: Oral reprimand

Step 2: Written reprimand

Step 3: Transfer

Step 4: Suspension

Step 5: Demotion

Step 6: Termination

Oral Reprimand

Oral reprimands are tools that will let firefighters know that their behavior is still unsatisfactory. Oral reprimands should be given by the evaluator, usually the company officer. They should be given in a private meeting. The fact that an oral reprimand has been issued should be kept confidential. The firefighter should be told that if the behavior continues, a written reprimand will be given (Figure 8.7).

Figure 8.7 If unsatisfactory behavior continues, the company officer should tell the firefighter that a written reprimand is the next step.

Written Reprimand

Written reprimands are basically written reports that indicate that a firefighter's unsatisfactory behavior has continued to go unchanged.

The reprimand should also be issued by the company officer. The firefighter should sign the reprimand indicating that he or she is aware of the continuing problem. A copy of the reprimand should then be put in the firefighter's permanent file.

Transfer

The next step in progressive discipline is a transfer to a new assignment. Company officers should realize that oral and written reprimands may result in a "transfer request" from the firefighter. Firefighters usually make this request to "get away from officers who are giving them a hard time." Whether a transfer is requested or results from punishment, the firefighter may take the behavior problem to the new assignment.

Whatever the case, officers who receive transferred firefighters must review the personnel file of the firefighter in order to know what step to take next if the problem continues. Transfers for personality reasons should be granted only once in a firefighter's career. If a second transfer is requested or necessary, the firefighter should be required to seek counseling as a condition of the transfer.

Suspension

Suspension procedures will usually be defined in department procedures and/or the union contract. When suspension is being considered, those documents must be consulted to determine the specific requirements for suspension. Suspension is punitive, and not an alternative to consider lightly. However, it is a strong motivator in some instances and has some value. A firefighter should not be suspended more than once in a five-year period and not more than two or three times in a career.

If the firefighter returns to the original undesired behavior after suspension, it should be obvious that some other method of behavior modification is necessary.

Demotion

Although tradition in the fire service runs contrary to demotion, it has become a tool in dealing with some behavior problems. Promotion, prestige, and position have been based for years on seniority. It was impossible to demote someone because the seniority system would be upset. Fortunately, this type of promotional system is disappearing in the modern fire service, and demotion is becoming a more popular management choice.

The underlying principle of demotion has been discussed in Lawrence J. Peter's *The Peter Principle,* which states an individual will be promoted to his or her level of incompetence. For example, an individual may be an excellent firefighter, but when promoted, the person may be a very poor apparatus operator. Logically, the best solution is to return the individual to a firefighter position. The department's tact in demoting an individual will greatly influence the individual's development.

If possible, the demotion should be handled discreetly and positively. The less an issue is made of the demotion, the easier it will be for the individual to adjust.

The department can expect the individual to file a union grievance, but this does not change the department's obligation to be discreet. It is often best to transfer the individual to another station when demoted.

Termination

Termination is used when all else has failed to bring the individual into accord with the requirements of the organization. It is the least desirable action in terms of department cost effectiveness.

Every effort should be made to salvage the individual while making it clear that certain behavior will result in termination.

DOCUMENTATION

All phases of discipline indicate a serious breach or impasse between the department and the individual. Most of these actions can be expected to result in a union grievance being filed. The company officer must keep accurate and detailed records.

The actual transfer, suspension, demotion, or termination will be made by a chief officer or department administrator. The company officer will become less involved in the administrative functions, but the officer's records will become essential. The officer's mental notes or recollections are not acceptable. Only official records—the station diary, employee evaluation, or other personnel forms—are acceptable in administrative actions.

EVALUATION TECHNIQUES FOR EFFECTIVE INTERVIEWS

The system of evaluation more or less hinges on the success of the formal evaluation session. The most important point is interaction between the firefighter and department. The company officer can use certain techniques or actions for smooth and effective evaluation interviews.

Firefighters probably will be receptive to the interview on one hand and anxious on the other. Individuals like to know about the good things they do, but will view portions of the interview as a report card and dread it. This anxiety can destroy the effectiveness of the entire evaluation if it is not properly recognized and handled.

To lessen the employee's anxiety, the supervisor first must plan the evaluation session. Begin by reviewing the firefighter's record and filling out the evaluation form. The company officer should then set an agenda for the session and arrange a time when they can meet. Select a time as free of interruptions or distractions as possible. Schedule a minimum of 30 minutes; the ideal time is about an hour.

Begin the session on time. Forcing the firefighter to sit and wait will only increase the anxiety he or she feels. If something comes up, the firefighter should be contacted immediately and an alternate time set up.

When the session starts, the furniture should be arranged so the firefighter can look directly at the officer without distractions (Figure 8.8). Seat the firefighter alongside the desk or avoid using a desk at all. Start the meeting by explaining that the session is a tool to help the firefighter advance in the organization. It should be made clear that the session is not designed to judge the firefighter, but to be a constructive career tool to help both the firefighter and the department.

After explaining the purpose of the agenda, review the firefighter's strengths and attributes. The firefighter should be told what personal behavior makes him or her an asset to the organization. This information will bolster the firefighter's feeling of belonging in the organization and increase his or her willingness to view the session as a favorable experience.

Figure 8.8 The communication process is enhanced if physical barriers, such as desks, are removed.

After covering the good points, the company officer should encourage the firefighter to talk about how he or she views the work and relationships within the department. The most important thing for the officer to do here is listen. It is not the time or place to dispute or correct the firefighter. The firefighter is encouraged to talk so the department can find out how the firefighter views himself or herself. It is more important that the firefighter express what he or she feels than whether the perspective is correct.

During this portion of the session, firefighters may ignore their own shortcomings, but may indicate where they want to go in the department. Through skillful listening, the company officer can discover how the firefighter feels about his or her relationship with the department.

The company officer, after listening to the firefighter, should try to deal with this perspective, and if possible, help the firefighter define how he or she feels. The officer can restate the firefighter's statements as a closed-ended question. "Firefighter Jones, do I understand correctly that you feel you will be ready for a driver position soon?" The firefighter can then confirm or deny this observation. If the firefighter denies it, an open-ended question such as, "Could you tell me again about how you feel about becoming a driver?" should follow to let the firefighter indicate his or her feelings more precisely.

When the firefighter has finished defining his or her feelings about the relationship with the department, the company officer should describe the changes the firefighter needs to make in his or her behavior. If the firefighter can relate the changes to the attainment of his or her goals, the firefighter will often view the changes as challenges instead of corrections. This positive feeling will develop in the firefighter a better mood to successfully complete these changes in behavior. If the changes are required simply to maintain the present position in the department, however, the firefighter must be so advised.

Weak points that the firefighter mentions during the interview should be recognized, but there is no real need to rehash them because the firefighter is aware they exist. An effective approach is to acknowledge them in a question that asks the firefighter to come up with a solution. "Firefighter Smith, you've noted that you feel you are weak on appearance. What do you think you can do to improve this area?" The firefighter should be urged to develop his or her own solutions (Figure 8.9).

Figure 8.9 Firefighters should be encouraged to develop their own solutions during the evaluation.

These solutions should be performance-measurable objectives. They should not require immediate, complete correction; rather, they should be arranged to let the firefighter progress toward correction. For example, goals could be "to pass 80 percent of the inspections up to the next evaluation without deficiencies" or "to complete all reports in the period following the evaluation without more than 5 percent being returned for correction." The company officer must be diligent not to set objectives that are beyond the firefighter's capabilities. For example, if the firefighter has never passed an inspection, it would be unwise and unfair to set this person a goal of passing 98 percent of all inspections.

Once the firefighter and the company officer agree on a course of action or solutions to the firefighter's deficiencies, the solutions should be written down and the firefighter should read them. The company officer should summarize the entire interview in closing, and the firefighter should be given the evaluation form afterward for review and signature. If the firefighter has any questions about the evaluation, they should be discussed before the session ends (Figure 8.10).

Figure 8.10 At the end of the interview, both parties should have a better understanding of each other and a positive growth direction.

COACHING GOAL-ORIENTED BEHAVIOR

An effective leader/manager helps people by cooperating to set meaningful goals. People work more diligently and efficiently when they have a verbalized description, not just some vague "understanding" or generalized expectations of where they are going. When a person sets a goal, he or she starts thinking how to achieve that goal. When a manager sets goals for people, the manager takes responsibility for their actions, basing influence on reward and coercive power. The manager must allow people to help set their goals so they can feel responsible for their actions. The manager thereby shows trust in their capabilities and concern for hearing their opinions and ideas. The ability to influence people becomes based partly on legitimate power, but mostly on identification power.

WHERE DO YOU STAND?

Feeling powerless is a major cause of tension in organizations, for it hinders organizational performance. The ineffective use of power leaves people feeling that one person or a small group of people run their lives. This chapter has examined five characteristics that facilitate the effective use of power.

If these ideas sound interesting (even if you do not totally agree with them), you may want to examine how your personnel perceive your exercise of influence and your behavior on the five characteristics discussed. In talking with them, listen for statements or concerns they might have about gaining power or keeping power they now have. Are they defensive about working decisions they have made when you ask about them? Do they make decisions without checking with you? Do they come to you with new ideas? Do they ask for your opinion on their failures as well as their successes? Do they feel that they have some control over achieving their performance goals? Do they feel their part of the organization is in continual conflict with another part of the organization?

Asking your personnel how they feel about your exercise of influence may lead to some rewarding discussion. It certainly will be an effective use of power.

SUMMARY

Employee evaluation is a career counseling tool used to determine if a firefighter is functioning relative to the needs of the department. Current standards that have minimum qualifications firefighters must pass to perform their job should be used during evaluations. Two questions to ask in determining if the firefighter's performance is compatible with the job are: Is the firefighter performing safely? Does the firefighter have good working relationships with others? The cycle of employee evaluation includes interaction with the firefighter, listening to the firefighter, recording desired behavior, modifying undesired behavior, and evaluating standards that may be inappropriate. If undesired behavior continues, discipline must be considered. The progressive steps of discipline are oral reprimand, written reprimand, transfers, suspension, demotion, and termination. Throughout the entire disciplinary process, the employee is entitled to due process under the law and representation, if desired. Any form of discipline must be supported by department records that pertain to the situation.

Evaluation interviews should be planned, and a definite agenda should be developed. The most important point to the evaluation interview is interaction. Allow firefighters to discuss their feelings as well as how they may fit into the organization. If there are problems, try to arrive at solutions jointly. This may be done by having the firefighter participate in setting goals. As a company officer you should also find out how the firefighters feel about you and the way you are leading them. Interaction like this may allow you to see where your strengths and weaknesses are.

SUPPLEMENTAL READINGS

Effective Supervisory Practices. 2nd ed. Washington D.C.: International City Management Association, 1984.

Gratz, David B. *Fire Department Management: Scope and Method*. Beverly Hills: Glencoe Press, 1972.

Management in the Fire Service. Didactic Systems, Inc. Boston: National Fire Protection Association, 1977.

9

Problem Solving

LESSON OBJECTIVES

After completing this chapter and related *Student Guide* applications, company officer candidates should be able to:

- Recall in the correct order the steps in the eight-step problem-solving process.

- Explain what is meant by curing symptoms instead of curing problems.

- State why the perfect solution may not be the best solution.

- Explain why the implementation of the solution must be carefully monitored.

- Demonstrate the ability to
  —Handle complaints.
  —Solve problems.
  —Introduce change.

This chapter addresses NFPA 1021,
Standard for Fire Officer Professional Qualifications (1987):
2-2.5   4-4.6
                         4-9.9.

Chapter 9
Problem Solving

Company officers must develop the necessary skills to become problem solvers. Officers face a complete spectrum of problems, ranging from logistics to involved personal problems. The officer's ultimate goal is to find effective solutions. Successful solutions are often obvious and easily implemented, but some problems simply do not have easy answers. The same methodical approach to problem solving can be applied to the less difficult as well as the most complex of situations. This method is called the eight-step method of problem resolution (Figure 9.1).

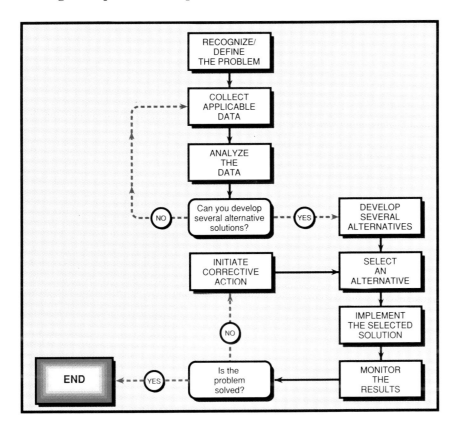

Figure 9.1 The eight-step method of problem resolution offers a sequential method of identifying and solving problems.

Step 1: Recognize and define the problem.

Step 2: Collect applicable data about the problem.

Step 3: Analyze the problem.

Step 4: Develop several alternatives.

Step 5: Select the best alternative.

Step 6: Implement the solution.

Step 7: Monitor the results.

Step 8: Take corrective action, if necessary.

PROBLEM RECOGNITION

During the recognition phase of problem solving, asking some basic questions will help pinpoint the problem:

- What brought the problem to the officer's attention?
- What are the symptoms?
  - Loss of property
  - Loss of productivity
  - Lower quality
  - Lower morale
  - Communication breakdown
- Who is involved?
- What is the standard? (Performance Standard or Standard Operating Procedure)

This checklist will define the problem if the officer is able to determine the correct answers. The most common failure in using the checklist is applying quick surface answers. Any solution must be based on correctly recognizing the problem; therefore, adequate time must be spent researching the checklist beyond obvious appearances. Information is best written down for reference during the implementation step.

COLLECTING DATA

After recognizing the problem, the officer must collect data before the problem can be analyzed. The number of facts the officer needs will depend on the nature of the problem and the amount of time available. The officer should never make assumptions during this stage of the problem-solving process.

Perhaps the hardest thing for a new officer to learn during the fact-finding stage is how to ask questions and take enough time to listen to the answers. Of course, there will be instances when time will not permit the officer to be a "Sherlock Holmes," but firefighters should be encouraged to provide as much information as possible. Often, the type of questions asked and how they are asked will determine how much information a firefighter provides. Closed-ended questions, which often can be answered with a yes or no, are poor choices when attempting to find facts. Open-ended questions, which require firefighters to explain their answers, are better for gathering information. Often, both types of questions can be used together to get to the bottom of the problem.

Closed-ended questions:
Joe, do you think there is a problem?
George, is there a fire inside?
Tom, do we have a problem with the truck?

Open-ended questions:
Joe, what do you think the problem is?
George, what is on fire inside?
Tom, what seems to be wrong with the truck?

The benefits of invoking firefighters' opinions are twofold. First, the firefighters may provide valuable clues to the nature of the problem or may have a solution to the problem. Second, since they are being involved in the solution, they have greater motivation. They feel their opinion is valued. This extra enthusiasm and involvement cannot be ordered, but can be generated by a good company officer.

ANALYZING

As soon as the information is compiled, the officer must review it (Figure 9.2). Irrelevant information should be discarded and important information earmarked for quick reference. The objective of the review is threefold: first, the information should

Figure 9.2 By reviewing all information compiled, relevant items should be separated and retained for further consideration.

form a basis for predicting the outcome of possible solutions. Second, the review will help determine the priority with which to handle the problem. Third, the review will help determine if additional information is necessary. Be aware that decisions must often be made without complete information.

A wise old fire chief used to tell his officers, "I pay you to make the best decision with the information available. If *all* the information were available, any idiot could make the right decision!"

DEVELOPING ALTERNATIVES

Once the problem has been analyzed, alternatives must be developed even when the solution seems obvious. The probable outcome, as predicted from the information gathered, should be matched with the suggested alternative. Sometimes it is useful to start by determining both the worst and the best possible alternatives. After the two extremes are determined, at least three intermediate alternatives should be developed. Each alternative should be written down with the predicted outcome.

SELECTING THE BEST ALTERNATIVE

With five or more possible alternatives, the search for the best solution can begin. There are five factors to consider when assessing the "best" alternative: the risk involved, the cost involved, the time available, resources available, and reaction to the solution (Figure 9.3).

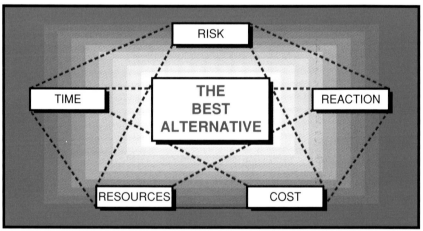

Figure 9.3 When choosing the best alternative, all variables are dependent on each other, and each must be considered as a part of the whole.

No alternative is without risk. The best alternative is the one that offers the greatest potential outcome for the degree of risk involved. Generally speaking, alternatives that involve possible injury or death cannot be balanced by potential outcome, except when the possible outcome is saving a life. Such a risk is NEVER justifiable to save property.

The cost of the alternative is also weighed against the possible outcome to determine the best decision. It does not take a genius to see that the best alternative will have the greatest possible outcome for the smallest investment. However, cost is always a secondary factor to risk. A high cost factor is more acceptable than an increased risk.

The time required to implement a solution must be considered against the time available. Problems typically set their own deadlines, although they may not be obvious. Time must be available to implement the alternative before the problem reaches its deadline. Problems do not wait for perfect solutions.

Resource needs may also eliminate alternatives. If an alternative requires resources that are not available, the alternative is more of a dream than a solution. Allocating limited resources often becomes a balancing function. Balancing the best possible results with the least resource (least cost) allocation is the mark of the best solution. Personnel is probably the most often overestimated and overextended resource. When picking a possible solution, calculate the personnel capability at the low average range instead of the highly efficient range. Often the situation worsens quickly enough that a highly efficient application of personnel is necessary to accomplish low average results.

IMPLEMENTING THE SOLUTION

The best solution, even the perfect solution, is worthless if incorrectly implemented. A good rule of thumb is that the implementation must solve more problems than it creates. Good implementation involves applying the management process.

MONITORING THE RESULTS

The results of the solution must be monitored to ensure proper implementation and to make sure the problem was corrected. The officer first must supervise implementation to detect efforts that do not help solve the problem, or that actually create other problems. A plan to solve a problem can fail for several reasons. The first and probably most common reason is that the solution was faulty. The officer must keep this possibility in mind as the situation develops.

After the solution has been implemented, the officer must constantly reassess the situation and determine if the problem has been positively or negatively affected. If the problem has been solved, the officer needs to continue monitoring the situation to make sure the problem does not recur. If the problem has not been solved or if implementation does not go smoothly, then the officer must take corrective action.

TAKING CORRECTIVE ACTION

Corrective action is necessary when the implementation is not effective or does not proceed correctly. If corrective action is necessary, go back to Step 2, "Collecting Data."

Many people apply solutions to problems without using the eight-step method, and their solution typically cures the symptoms only, postponing the solution to the problem. The following example illustrates the way in which the eight-step problem-solving method works:

> The chief requested that the station captain determine how injuries were sustained by firefighters responding to various emergencies. The chief was concerned that the department's standard operating policy did not adequately address firefighter safety. In addition, the chief wanted to know practical ways the department could raise the level of safety.

Step 1: The problem has been recognized and defined by the chief and left for the captain to solve.

Step 2: The captain needs to find and collect data about the issues of firefighter safety while responding to the scene of an emergency. This might be accomplished by contacting the department's vehicle insurance company, contacting the research department of the National Fire Protection Association, researching information at a local library, or reviewing annual statistics on firefighter injuries published by several trade magazines.

Step 3: Analyze the collected data and apply information that is applicable to the conditions or situations that the department faces. Does the department have long or short distances for response? Does the department have firefighter safety devices on the apparatus? Questions should be raised on every aspect that may affect or contribute to firefighter injury or death while responding to the scene.

Step 4: Next, develop several alternatives for the chief to consider that would reduce the frequency and severity of accidents. These may include changes in procedures, methods of driving, additional training for drivers, or installation of protective devices on the apparatus. Concentration of enforcement of departmental policies may also be an alternative.

Step 5: Select the best one or two alternatives. This may be done by the person in charge of problem solving or by seeking advise from others who are familiar with the problem. The result should be an effective change for the department that will reduce the likelihood that a firefighter will be injured while responding to the scene.

Step 6: Implement the solution that has been proposed. Require that new methods or procedures be followed or that the new safety devices be installed. Carry out the proposal.

Step 7: Monitor the results. For a designated period of time, watch for results that indicate the solution is or is not having an effect on the problem. Be sure to allow a reasonable time for the results to show. In this example, 12 to 18 months may be needed for an indication that a safety device or procedure is working.

Step 8: Take corrective action, if necessary. This step may be left out if the solution provides the exact answer to the problems that were identified. This step may also be useful to allow modification or slight changes so that the solution accomplishes the given goal.

HANDLING COMPLAINTS

Complaints are problems, but they are special because they involve someone's feelings. For this reason, it is hard to apply the problem-solving process to complaints. Ideally, the officer's objective in handling complaints should be to separate the feelings from the problem and then apply the problem-solving process to the problem.

To separate the problem from the feelings, officers must know why people complain. Basically, people complain because they perceive a problem that adversely affects them. Often, an individual feels the situation involves a personal slight (Figure 9.4 on next page). Firefighters complain for four basic reasons:

- To bring about change
- To release pressure
- To get attention
- To confront personality conflicts

The officer must keep these reasons in mind while handling the complaint. The solution to the problem will come from the problem-solving method, but to handle the feelings, it is important to determine the reason behind the complaint.

To deal with the complaint, the officer should set a time when the firefighter and the officer can talk alone. The company officer must keep in mind that even though a complaint may seem trivial, the feelings involved may make it very important to the individual. For this reason, the individual deserves a private opportunity to discuss the complaint. If the officer fails to provide a chance to air the complaint, the situation can worsen without the officer having a second chance to intervene.

Figure 9.4 Firefighters may complain for various reasons; but, it is the company officer's duty to listen and resolve the conflict.

When the session begins, the officer should be a listener. However, the officer may need to aid the individual by asking open-ended questions. These questions should attempt to determine:

- What the individual perceives as the problem
- Who the individual feels is involved
- What the individual sees as a possible solution to the problem
- What the individual expects the officer to do

As the individual answers these questions, it should become clear where the problem separates from the personal feelings. The officer should help the individual see the difference, using open-ended and reflective questions, which repeat the individual's previous statement in the form of a question.

> Firefighter: "I really like this shift, but some guys really bother me."
> Officer: "You really like this shift, but there are some guys who bother you?"

The reflective question gives the individual a chance to expand on the comment and assures the officer that the individual really meant to say that. Sometimes a reflective statement can be combined with an open-ended question to encourage the individual to talk.

Officer: "You really like the shift, but there are some guys who bother you? How do they bother you?"

When the officer can separate the feelings from the problems, the officer should be able to determine what can be done about the problem, using the problem-solving method. Then the feelings about the problem should be addressed. The bad feelings do not have to be resolved, but the officer must demonstrate that the firefighter's feelings have been recognized, that the individual's well being is important, and that there are plans to help correct the situation. In closing, the officer should recap the conversation by stating:

- What the problem appears to be
- What solution is planned
- That the officer is aware of the individual's personal feelings
- That the officer is interested
- That the officer will follow up on the problem

THE CHRONIC COMPLAINER

Most individuals will have complaints from time to time, a natural result of people working together. However, there are certain individuals who chronically complain. Everything bothers these individuals and everyone is trying to "get" them. The company officer who has a chronic complainer indeed has a problem (Figure 9.5). In these instances, the officer must work

Figure 9.5 A chronic complainer is a serious situation that cannot be ignored; action is required before company morale is affected.

hard to understand why the complainer persists. Generally, chronic complainers are dissatisfied with themselves, or feel insecure or inferior. For these reasons, the normal complaint process will have short-term effects at best.

The best method for handling the chronic complainer is to arrange tasks that will provide a reasonable chance of success and high visibility. If chronic complainers are producing something they can be proud of, they will focus more on their achievements than their alleged misfortunes. If the chronic complaining does not cease, the company officer should consult superiors about advising the individual to seek professional psychiatric help. A chronic complainer is someone who cannot be ignored. Firefighters will never get used to it. The chronic complainer will make everyone in the company miserable and destroy company morale and effectiveness. The last resort is to remove the individual from the company by transfer to a more appropriate job or by dismissal.

SUMMARY

The company officer is a key individual in the problem-solving process. First, the problems need to be identified and the proper perspective taken. Perhaps what seems to be a problem is merely a misunderstanding of terms, information, or perspective. In that case, the problem is readily solved by clarifying the issue.

If it is determined that there is a problem, then the officer can pool resources to assist in problem solving. This would require that every member of the officer's group concentrate on the problem being addressed. Then, the group members should begin to seek out the needed information that will help solve the problem. The entire process should become an organized group effort. The officer must then use the information gathered to make a final decision to solve the problem. Complaints should be dealt with first at the company level. The officers should talk with the firefighter and try to resolve the problem. Chronic complainers should be dealt with quickly. If a complainer is allowed to continue, the company morale and sense of togetherness will be lost.

SUPPLEMENTAL READINGS

Effective Supervisory Practices. 2nd ed. Washington D.C.: International City Management Association, 1984.

Gratz, David B. *Fire Department Management: Scope and Method*. Beverly Hills: Glencoe Press, 1972.

Management in the Fire Service. Didactic Systems, Inc. Boston: National Fire Protection Association, 1977.

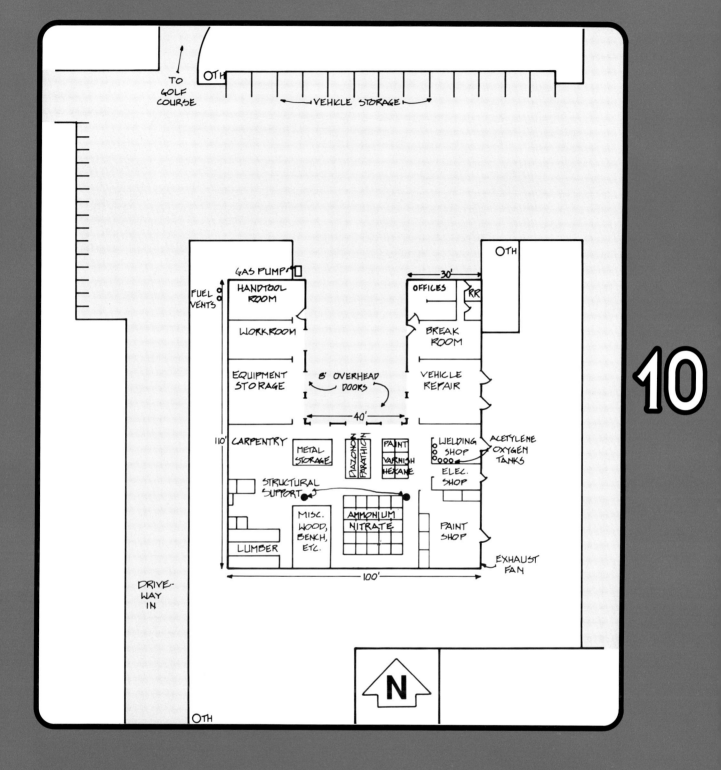

Pre-Incident Surveys

LESSON OBJECTIVE

After completing this chapter and related *Student Guide* applications, company officer candidates should be able to:

- Distinguish between pre-incident surveys and pre-incident planning.

- Recognize the purposes of pre-incident surveys.

- Discuss the importance of pre-incident surveys.

- Illustrate and explain the importance of accurate sketches and photographs compiled during a pre-incident survey.

- Understand the role of the company officer as a member of the pre-incident survey team.

- Demonstrate the ability to
  —Measure hydrant flow with a pitot tube.
  —Direct a pre-incident survey team on site.
  —Delegate duties and supervise pre-incident report drawings and write-up.

This chapter addresses NPFA 1021,
Standard for Fire Officer Professional Qualifications (1987):
2-4.1	4-10.4.
2-10.6	

Chapter 10
Pre-Incident Surveys

Pre-incident surveys are essential for developing strategy. The pre-incident survey basically consists of sending the company to a selected site to gather information. It is a good method for obtaining the necessary information for developing fire suppression or other emergency plans. Upon completion of the on-site visit, the company officer is responsible for writing and forwarding a report to the fire department administration. Chief officers use these reports to develop information resource systems and strategic plans. Although the entire evaluation and information-gathering process is referred to as pre-incident planning, it actually consists of three separate fire department functions:

- The pre-incident survey

- Development and implementation of procedures

- Development of information resource systems

Pre-incident planning has several characteristics that make the process a positive and effective tool in reducing fire and life loss. Pre-incident planning is a result of collective efforts from all levels of the fire department, beginning with the company performing the on-site facility survey. The information gathered allows the fire department to coordinate resources to meet special demands within its jurisdiction (Figure 10.1 on next page). The success of the pre-incident planning process depends upon the ability of the company to perform adequate pre-incident surveys and to forward complete, accurately written reports and information.

The company officer should recognize the difference between pre-incident planning and the pre-incident survey. Pre-incident planning is the whole process of gathering information, developing procedures, and maintaining information resource systems.

Figure 10.1 Facility surveys allow the company an opportunity to accurately determine pre-incident planning strategies.

The pre-incident survey is the fact-gathering part of pre-incident planning. The task of performing pre-incident surveys is done at the company level for several reasons:

- To allow the firefighters to become familiar with the building, its physical layout and design, and its associated hazards

- To give the firefighters a chance to visualize how the existing strategies apply to the building

- To allow the firefighters to recognize new hazards that were not noted during previous facility surveys

For these reasons, pre-incident surveys serve a double purpose: information gathering and training.

The fire department administration should specify how the company officer is to conduct the pre-incident survey. Although the company officer may not have much input into the decision, he or she is obliged to know the department's facility survey policy. One way the fire department can coordinate the facility survey program is by having staff personnel make facility survey appointments and assign the companies to perform the facility survey. Another way is to give the company officer written guidelines and require that he or she schedule the facility surveys in that company's district.

The method of administering the program is not a major consideration for the company officer; nonetheless, he or she must ensure a productive working relationship between the property tenant and the fire department. It is difficult to perform adequate facility surveys without the support of the property tenant (Figure 10.2).

The key to developing a suitable working relationship between the company officer and the tenant is respect and under-

Figure 10.2 The company officer must work together with the building tenant to adequately perform a proper facility survey.

standing. The company officer should begin by having the facility survey scheduled at a time convenient for the tenant. Mercantile facility surveys, for example, should not be attempted during peak shopping seasons such as Christmas, Easter, or the tourist season. Instead, facility surveys of industrial or public assembly occupancies can be scheduled during those times.

When scheduling the facility survey, the company officer should explain the purpose of the survey to the tenant. If this cannot be done when the appointment is made, the officer should give an explanation before conducting the facility survey. An important point to communicate to the tenant is the benefits to the occupancy such as enhanced capability to save the structure and its contents. The company officer should make every effort to be cordial and tactfully honest during the facility survey.

The company officer must attempt to have the inspection scheduled in conjunction with other department facility surveys. Often, the tenant will not understand that a pre-incident survey is different from a recent fire code enforcement inspection. This misunderstanding may result in the tenant viewing the facility survey as a form of harassment and may break down previously established working relationships.

The officer should strive to ensure that there is enough time to complete the facility survey properly. The quality of the facility survey is far more important than the quantity of facility surveys conducted. To complete the facility survey in one day is most convenient, but not essential. The company officer should make certain that the tenant realizes it may be necessary for a company member to return for additional information.

CONSIDERATIONS WHEN MAKING THE FACILITY SURVEY

Making a pre-incident survey begins by understanding that the survey is conducted to gather the information necessary for the fire department to protect the building and its contents from fire. Information concerning life safety, fire control, and property conservation must be gathered. When personnel understand the reasons for the facility survey, they can begin planning how to conduct the inspection.

Planning begins by reviewing information about the type of business to be inspected to get an idea of what type of problems to expect. If the fire department has a standard pre-incident survey form, it can be used to simplify planning. If the fire department does not provide a standard form, the company can develop one while planning the facility survey.

The first priority of the facility survey is to identify life safety concerns. Life safety information is collected in two basic areas: protection and evacuation of occupants, and protection of the firefighters. Information about occupant protection includes the following:

- Location and size of entrances and exits
- Location of escalators and elevators
- Location of windows suitable for rescue access
- Special rescue problems such as handicapped occupants, very old or very young occupants, and large numbers of occupants
- Flammable and toxic interior finishes or processes

As firefighters gather information about occupant life safety, they are recording information about hazards in the building that will threaten their own safety (Figure 10.3). It is often

Figure 10.3 Documenting hazardous conditions while on location increases the accuracy of the observations.

helpful to photograph these hazards to get a clearer idea of the danger they present. Some of the first hazards to be aware of are the following:

- Flammable and combustible liquids

- Toxic chemicals

- Explosives

- Reactive metals

- Radioactive materials

- Processes performed in the building that are inherently dangerous

In addition to the contents of the building, note physical conditions of the structure that may be hazardous during a fire. Such conditions include:

- Structural components that could fail during a fire
  —Construction material that might lose its strength when exposed to fire (for example, steel and lime mortar)
  —Ornamental building facings, awnings, and marquees
  —Unsupported partitions or walls
  —Roof construction

- Conditions in the building that can become dangerous during a fire
  —Stacked or high-piled storage
  —Utility equipment on the roof that can cause roof collapse
  —Heavy equipment that may fall through a floor or cause the floor to collapse during a fire

- Physical features of the building that might confuse or trap the firefighter during the fire
  —Large open areas
  —Dead-end corridors or hallways
  —Open vats, pits, or holes
  —Openings into underground utility shafts or tunnels
  —Multilevel floor arrangement
  —Mazelike room divisions or partitions

Fire Control

It will be necessary to gather information in order to control a fire in the building (Figure 10.4 on next page). Although not directly related to fire control, the following information about the business is included under this heading.

- The address

- The street location

- The type of business and content hazards

PRE-INCIDENT PLAN SURVEY

------ COMMERCIAL OCCUPANCY ASSESSMENT -----------------

DATE	COMPANY MAKING ASSESSMENT

PROPERTY NAME	ADDRESS	PHONE

PROPERTY OWNER	PHONE	NAME OF LESSEE, RENTER, ETC.	PHONE

DESCRIPTION

CONSTRUCTION	
AREA	HEIGHT	YEAR BUILT
# OF STORIES	FLOOR CONSTRUCTION
ROOF CONSTRUCTION	

STRUCTURAL INFO

ELEVATORS	#	LOCATION
ATTIC	ACCESSIBILITY BY STAIRS
BASEMENT	AREA
EMERGENCY LIGHTING	LOCATION

LIFE HAZARD

OCCUPANCY	
DAY	NIGHT
HANDICAP FACILITIES	MEANS OF EGRESS
FIRE NOTIFICATION FOR THE DEAF	
HANDICAP CONSTRUCTION EGRESS MEANS	

RESIDENT INFO

LIVING QUARTERS	#	GENERAL LOCATION
HANDICAP OCCUPANTS	#	GENERAL LOCATION
CLASS		GENERAL LOCATION

UTILITIES

GAS	WATER	ELECTRIC

HAZARDOUS MATERIALS

LOCATION	LOCATION
MATERIAL	MATERIAL
QUANTITY	QUANTITY

FIRE SUPPRESSION/DETECTION SYSTEMS

AUTOMATIC FIRE ALARM	# OF BELLS	REGULAR FIRE DRILLS
BUILDING SPRINKLERS	TYPE	PARTIAL SYSTEM LOCATION
SPECIAL SYSTEM	TYPE	LOCATION

STANDPIPE SYSTEM DRY WET	LOCATION	HOUSE LINES	LOCATION	ADAPTER NEEDED

Figure 10.4 This Commercial Occupancy Assessment form is an excellent method of gathering and organizing information during facility survey.

- Owner/tenant information
- Whom to contact on the premises
- The working hours
- The number of people who may be in the building during different times

The company should think about any response problems or building access complications. These problems include:

- Traffic
  —Bridges
  —Railroads
  —Freeways
  —Terrain
  —Overhead obstructions
  —Special traffic problems (for example, school zones and business districts)
- Elevation differences between the street level and the building
- Forcible entry problems
- Security problems

The construction of the building is a major fire control factor. The type and materials of construction must be included in the survey information. The actual materials used in the construction may vary. Factors include region, design, aesthetics, or function. It is important that all firefighters understand building construction theory and application. It is *imperative* that the company officer not only understand these theories, but also have a working knowledge of their application during tactical operations (Figure 10.5). Consult the IFSTA validated **Building**

Figure 10.5 It is important that the company officer have a working knowledge of building construction in theory and application.

Construction manual for more information about building construction and how it concerns the fire service.

An important fire control factor about which the company must obtain data is the water supply. This information should include the locations and flow test results for any fire hydrants that would be used to fight a fire in the building. The location of secondary hydrants should also be noted. An estimate of the needed maximum fire flow for the building should be developed. Consult IFSTA's validated **Water Supply** manual for fire flow determination theory and procedures.

Private fire protection equipment in the building is also an important consideration. The presence of sprinkler systems, standpipes, alarm systems, and any other equipment should be noted in the facility survey. Proper operating instructions for any equipment should also be obtained. During the facility survey, the company should check to make sure that any water supply equipment has connections that match fire department threads.

Ventilation information is obtained next to indicate possible ventilation tactics. Information about the heating and air conditioning (HVAC) system and its operation for ventilation is important. The location of any vertical shafts in the building should be noted. Roof construction and the presence of any roof openings should be recorded. Routes of access to the roof and suitable ladder placement locations are important considerations. Any overhead obstructions or other factors that will reduce the capabilities of aerial equipment should also be noted.

Also included in fire control is exposure protection. Exposures within the building receive initial consideration, especially floors above probable fire locations. Other internal exposure problems include such situations as a large structure divided into several small shops. In some cases, these partitions will not help slow the fire spread, but will reduce hoseline mobility; therefore, it is important to note their presence.

The second exposure consideration is any adjoining buildings. Openings between buildings or sections of buildings divided by a fire wall will be important locations to cover to prevent fire spread. In addition to openings, any utility casements or heat conductive materials that pass through the wall or floors should be noted.

Adjacent buildings or property are also important exposure considerations (Figure 10.6). Typically, buildings to the side are primary exposures; a building to the rear is a secondary exposure. The building across the street is the least important exposure; however, many cases have been recorded where a fire has spread

Figure 10.6 Adjacent buildings and property are important considerations during facility surveys.

across the street. Remaining exposure considerations include ground cover, fire equipment, utilities, bystanders, and the environment.

Property Conservation

The final area that the company officer should consider when making a facility survey is property conservation. The question that should be asked is: "What can the fire department do that will most reduce property loss?" A possible starting point for answering this question is to check for contents with a high value. Such items include files and records, electronic equipment, machinery, musical instruments, antiques, or any item that is not replaceable. To reduce or eliminate property damage, salvage efforts should be directed toward high-value items.

Next, consider items that will be harmed by water. If there are such items in the building, alternative methods of fire suppression should be examined. The best course of action is to explain the problem to the property owner and suggest that he or she consult a fire protection engineer. Items that may be susceptible to water damage include electronic equipment, chemicals, paper and products that are highly water absorptive, and bare-metal finished machinery.

The problem with water-absorbent materials is not necessarily the value of the product, but the weight of the water absorbed. The weight of the water and product may cause structural collapse or make cleanup extremely expensive.

The building should be examined to determine whether there are facilities that can be used to aid salvage. These facilities include scuttles, floor drains, sump pumps, materials that can be used for salvage covers, and stairways or halls that can be used to channel water out of the building. It is appropriate at this point in the facility survey to determine whether additional salvage equipment might be necessary on the first alarm. This can be done by comparing the amount of equipment that probably will be needed to the amount of equipment on the apparatus.

Facility Survey Equipment

Each fire company will need certain equipment and materials to conduct the facility survey. It is advantageous to collect the basic equipment and store it in a suitable container. This facility survey equipment kit should be taken with the company on all facility surveys (Figure 10.7). The equipment kits should include:

- Writing equipment (pads of paper, pencils, pencil sharpener, eraser, clipboard, straightedge, and any department facility survey forms)

Figure 10.7 The inspection kit contains all necessary materials used to conduct a facility survey.

- Drawing equipment (engineering or graph paper, architect's scale, protractor, and a copy of the mapping symbols used by the department or NFPA standard symbols)

- Other equipment (flashlight, portable radio, pitot tube, 50- or 100-foot measuring tape, and pertinent reference material such as the local fire code and an inspection manual)

- Hard hat, steel-toed shoes, eye protection (goggles or safety glasses, gloves, and any other items appropriate for personal protection)

Systematic Approach

Begin the facility survey by assigning each member to a specific task, briefing them on what is included in that task. Upon arrival at the facility survey location, the company members should remain at the apparatus while the company officer contacts the tenant.

The company officer should make the initial contact with the tenant, confirm the appointment, and brief the tenant on the facility survey procedure. The officer should indicate the number of company members that will be involved in the facility survey and specify any assistance the tenant should provide. The officer should also explain that any serious fire hazards found will have to be corrected. When serious hazards are found, the best approach for the officer is to attempt to obtain an on-the-spot correction and to send a follow-up memo to the fire prevention division.

After initial contact with the tenant, company members can begin the exterior facility survey of the building. Primarily, the exterior facility survey will deal with obtaining the necessary information for the plot plan. The building dimensions should be measured, including distances to exposures. The location of fire hydrants and valves, utility shutoffs, fences, landscaping, wire, obstructions, sprinkler and standpipe connections, and any underground tanks should be noted on the plot plan. During the exterior examination, information about the exposures should be collected. The building height can be determined while doing the exterior facility survey; however, the exterior of the building is not a good vantage point for gathering construction information. Many buildings are faced with brick and rock or covered with aluminum siding. Note any ornamental facings, awnings, or marquees while doing the exterior facility survey. Also note the location of doors, windows, and fire escapes.

After the exterior has been inspected, the company should move either to the roof of the building or to the lowest floor. Some officers find it helpful and less confusing to start on the roof. Continue the interior facility survey by making a floor plan of each floor, showing the location of permanent walls, partitions, fixtures, and machinery. Furniture should not be included in the floor plan because of its mobility. The locations of any vertical shafts and horizontal openings should be noted. The location of any fire protection equipment should be included on the floor plan, as should any life safety information.

TYPES OF BUILDING CONSTRUCTION

Determine the type of building construction while inside the building. If the building construction type is not clear, a further check with the building department or the fire prevention division may be necessary. It is usually easier to examine the type of construction while on the roof or in the attic. Unfinished basements are also excellent sources of construction information. Modifications of the original construction should be noted in detail. A memo noting these modifications should be forwarded to the fire prevention division and building department to ensure that the modification has not changed the code compliance of the building.

Facility Survey Drawings

Some of the information gathered during the facility survey is best forwarded as a written report. Information about the building layout, however, is more effectively conveyed by a drawing. Field sketches should be made during the facility survey and, after returning to the station, a legible, neat drawing made. These drawings should include all of the necessary pre-incident survey information.

The Field Sketch

The field sketch is a rough drawing of the building prepared during the facility survey. This drawing should show general information about floor plans, building dimensions, and such other related outside information as fire hydrants, streets, exposure distances, and permanent objects of importance (Figure 10.8). All the basic information for the report drawing should be shown on the field sketch, but all the details need not be included.

It is not important to draw the sketch to scale, but it is helpful to draw the sketch in proportion, using a straightedge. This will make it easier to transfer the information onto the report drawing.

The Report Drawing

The report drawing should be drawn to scale, showing the details of the building and its surroundings. The details should be shown neatly with standard mapping symbols. A ledger explaining the symbols must be included on or attached to the draw-

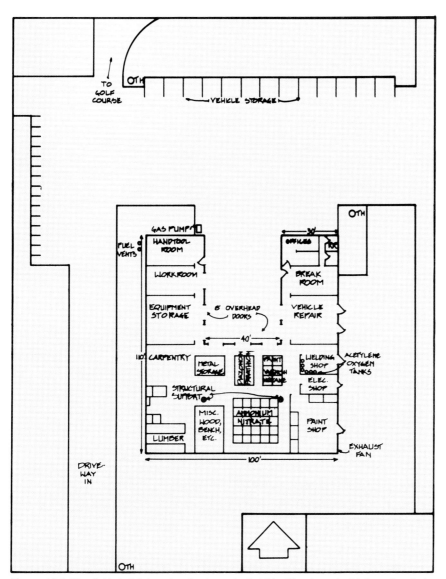

Figure 10.8 The field sketch is a drawing to scale that identifies important information that can be used for pre-incident strategic planning.

ing. Only standard symbols adopted by the department should be used. If an item must be included for which there is no standard symbol, use a circled numeral. Include an explanation of the material in an appendix attached to the drawing.

Types Of Drawings

There are three general types of drawings used to show building information: the plot plan, the floor plan, and the elevation drawing. The plot plan is used to indicate how the building is situated with respect to other buildings and streets in the area. The floor plan shows the layout of individual floors and the roof. Most of the building detail can be shown on the floor plan. The elevation drawing is used to show the number of floors in the building and the grade of the surrounding ground.

When inspecting small buildings, all the information can often be put onto one drawing, but as the building size or complexity increases, the number of drawings needed to show the necessary detail clearly will also increase. Every drawing or page of a set of maps should be labeled with a title that clearly indicates what type of information is included on the map.

After the report has been compiled in a clear, concise form, attach legible notes to the illustrations. The cover of the report should indicate such basic information as the address, the date of the facility survey, the type of building, and the submitting officer.

Using Photography

Photography is, at times, more advantageous than drawings when illustrating certain situations. Photography is an *exact* recording of the area; a drawing is an *interpretation* of an area.

The amount of detail shown is at the discretion of the inspector. Photographs can be used in addition to drawings. They add realism. Photographs can be taken during a facility survey and studied at a later date to determine tactical or strategic operations. In addition, detailed drawings (in conjunction with the field sketch) can be created from photographs.

The department should invest in a camera system that includes at a minimum the following equipment:

- A 35 mm single lens reflex camera (SLR)
- An electronic flash
- Wide angle (28 mm - 35 mm) and telephoto (85 mm -135 mm) lenses *or* a 28 mm - 135 mm zoom lens
- A durable camera bag

There are a multitude of accessories to enhance subject matter that can be added to the system once the basics are obtained; however, personnel must become competent with basic photography techniques. For example, a polarizing filter can completely eliminate glare and increase detail substantially if used properly. If the photographer does not understand why, when, or how to use this filter, the result can be an unusable image. The best equipment is useless if no one knows how to operate it properly.

With continuing advancements in technology, 35 mm cameras are becoming easier to operate; however, it is recommended that personnel designated to use the camera equipment complete a basic photography course. These courses usually include light and exposure control, basics of film, using electronic flashes, differences among lenses, and basic rules of composition. Advanced photography courses are also very beneficial. They would include additional lighting techniques, use of filters for image enhancement, compound exposure situations, film theory, and selection.

Although a 35 mm camera system is somewhat expensive, the investment is relatively low because the return is so high. A camera can be used for in-service facility surveys, during arson investigation, fire cause determination, public fire education, fire facility surveys, incidents, department promotions, and training. Some departments have realized the importance of photography and staff full-time photographers; other departments designate members of each shift.

ROLE OF THE COMPANY OFFICER

The company officer is the leader of the facility survey team. He or she is responsible for ensuring that the facility survey is performed in the most efficient and professional manner. Before leaving for the facility survey site, the company officer should review helpful information, including previous facility surveys, departmental facility survey methods and policies, and incident records. The company officer should expect to receive questions about the facility survey from both the tenant and members of the facility survey team. A prepared officer will be able to answer any questions professionally.

PUBLIC RELATIONS

The success of a departmental facility survey program relies on the manner in which the facility survey team conducts themselves and on the image they project. To be successful, facility survey teams must present a positive public image. Team members should be in dress uniform (Figure 10.9). They should also respect the needs and the operational problems of the tenants.

Conducting business in a courteous manner is of primary importance. If team members are abusive or rude, there is no chance that they will be accepted with a positive attitude. A bad facility survey at one establishment can also affect the image that tenants at other businesses have of the facility survey team. A store owner who has rude firefighters performing the inspection will no doubt tell other owners of his experience. For the sake of the facility survey program, the company officer must ensure that the image of the facility survey team is positive throughout the community.

CODES AND STANDARDS

There are different codes and standards that are useful to the facility survey team. Team leaders should be aware of the codes or standards that have been adopted by their jurisdiction. Examples of these codes and standards are the *Basic Building Code, Uniform Building and Fire Code, Southern Standard Building Code, and Life Safety Code.*

Figure 10.9 A company officer in uniform projects a professional image and usually results in a higher degree of cooperation with the building management.

SUMMARY

In-service company facility surveys are an important tool in the pre-incident planning process. The facility survey team should focus on hazards to life and property, resources available for fire control, and features that might help in property conservation efforts. Facility surveys give firefighters an idea what to expect if faced with an emergency at a particular location. The company officer is responsible for the behavior and conduct of the facility survey team and should be prepared to answer questions from both building occupants and facility survey team members. If in-service company facility surveys are handled with professionalism, the survey program has a high chance of success.

SUPPLEMENTAL READINGS

Fire Prevention and Code Enforcement. 5th ed. Stillwater, Okla.: Fire Protection Publications, Oklahoma State University, 1987.

Management in the Fire Service. Didactic Systems, Inc. Boston: National Fire Protection Association, 1977.

Managing Fire Services. Washington, D.C.: International City Management Association, 1979.

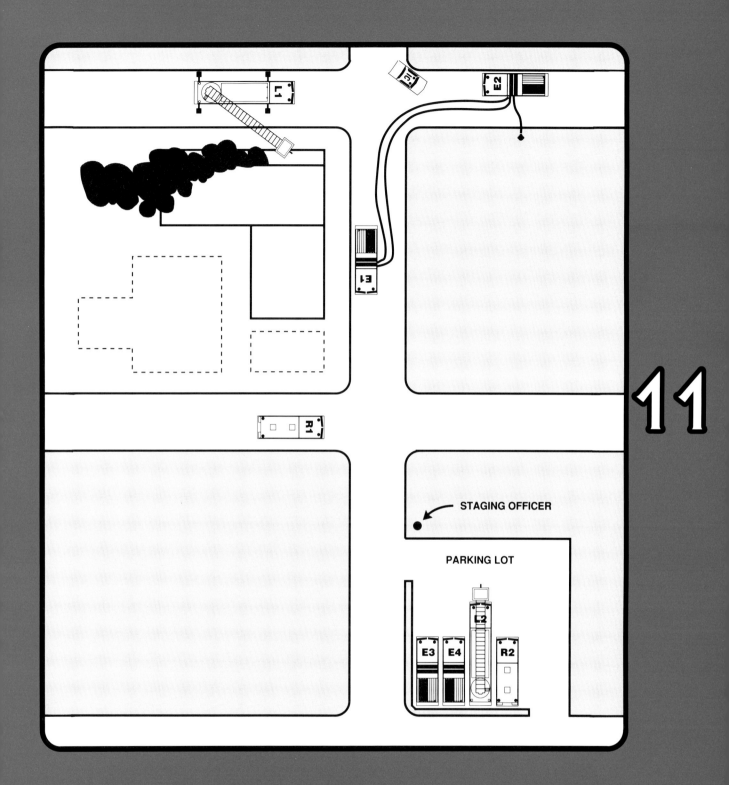

Fireground
Management

LESSON OBJECTIVE

After completing this chapter and related *Student Guide* applications, company officer candidates should be able to:

- Recall the fireground goal.

- Recognize the steps in developing a strategic plan.

- Describe the different attack modes and tell when they can be used.

- Distinguish among strategic plans, operational strategies, tactics, and standard operating procedures (SOPs).

- Explain how operational strategies are determined.

- Describe the tactical development process and its effect on operational strategies.

- Demonstrate the ability to develop a strategic plan for managing a hypothetical fireground.

This chapter addresses NFPA 1021;
Standard for Fire Officer Professional Qualifications (1987):

2-2.3	2-10.5
2-5.1	2-10.6
2-5.4	2-10.7
2-8.2	2-10.8
2-8.3	2-10.9
2-9.1	2-10.10
2-9.2	2-10.11
2-10.1	2-13.13
2-10.2	

Chapter 11

Fireground Management

The company officer typically initiates fire department action at an incident scene. For this reason, the company officer must have a sound base in fireground management, which necessitates an awareness of the fireground goal:

> **Protect life and property from fire loss by using operational strategies and tactics based on pre-incident planning, sound experience, training, and facts gathered as the incident progresses.**

By examining the fireground goal, several fundamental facts should become evident. First, the company officer should use the same management skills on the fireground as used in the station. Second, the fireground is not the place to develop strategic plans. Strategic plans are based on departmental standard operating procedures, training, pre-incident surveys, and other information gathered before a fire situation exists. Third, the company officer must be able to constantly monitor the fireground situation and employ suitable operational strategies and tactics as the situation changes.

STRATEGIC PLANS

Developing strategic plans is a continual process that begins at the administrative level of the department and extends down to the company level. Strategic plans are the broad objectives that determine how to solve a problem. They are written into the department's standard operating procedures and are based on information gathered before a fire is reported. Basic fire fighting strategy begins before the fire has started, not after.

Strategic planning begins with hazard recognition. Ideally, the fire department recognizes fire hazards when building contractors present plans for review. The fire department can then make changes and require the contractor to install protective equipment during construction. These changes should decrease the potential hazards facing firefighters and occupants when fire occurs in the facility.

In-Service Company Inspections

Pre-incident planning and fire prevention inspections are also good ways to recognize hazards. These occasions are excellent opportunities for the fire department to recognize and evaluate potential problems (Figure 11.1). Unfortunately, some hazards cannot be eliminated, so the fire department must develop a strategic plan to deal with them.

Figure 11.1 The company, as a team, should discuss potential hazards while at the site.

As soon as the hazard has been recognized, data should be collected and analyzed to develop the strategic plans. Data is collected by a number of methods. Some departments send out yearly questionnaires to local occupancies asking for information. Many departments organize pre-incident planning visits to gather information from target hazards in the jurisdiction. Data may also be compiled from fire code enforcement inspections, incident reports, and by studying target hazard properties.

When sufficient information is known about the hazard, information about available department resources must be compiled and analyzed. This search generally is in four areas: equipment, personnel, water, and private protection.

The company officer should be extensively involved in assessing the capabilities of the company's equipment and personnel. It is the responsibility of the company officer to know the capabilities of the company and the expectations placed upon it.

It is also important to make sure the company is not expected to provide an impossible level of service.

The third step in developing a strategic plan is to analyze the data and develop a range of strategies. The analysis must define the possibilities of the hazard, but should focus on the probabilities of the situation. For example, two 5-alarm fires might occur at the same time, but the probability is so small that a strategy for such an event is not a primary concern. After defining both possibilities and probabilities, the fire department should identify a range of probable emergencies and match the available department resources to meet them.

Once a probable emergency has been identified, the first determination to be made is the response assignment. The response assignment defines how much of the department's resources will be committed to a certain alarm. Alarm assignments should be graduated to initially commit only the resources necessary to handle the most probable situation. This initial assignment is commonly called the first-alarm assignment. Additional assignments or alarms are then developed to define the order in which remaining resources will be assigned. Alarm assignments also should include reassigning other companies to maintain uniform community coverage.

The next portion of the strategic plan to be developed is the attack mode. The concept of mode indicates that not all fires or emergencies will be in the same stage of advancement when the fire department receives the alarm; therefore, the fire department must provide a range of acceptable responses (modes) for first-arriving units. The two main attack modes are the offensive attack and the defensive attack.

OFFENSIVE FIRE ATTACK

An offensive fire attack is an aggressive interior attack. Fire conditions allow handlines to be advanced into the fire area (Figure 11.2). The offensive attack is often combined with primary search and rescue activities and usually requires coordinated forcible entry and ventilation operations. This is a fast-moving operation to control the fire in the area of origin before it has a chance to spread.

Fire department policies should dictate that fire-ground commanders use an offensive attack anytime conditions will permit it. In *Fire Command*, Chief Alan Brunacini of the Phoenix Fire Department suggests seven major criteria that will assist in determining attack mode:

- How much fire is in the structure and where is it located?

- What effect is the fire having on the structural components of the building?

Figure 11.2 Handlines are usually advanced during an offensive fire attack. *Courtesy of David Wiist, Edmond Fire Department, Edmond, OK.*

- How many persons are in the building and what is their condition?
- How much property is there to be saved?
- Can a crew or crews enter the structure and stay in long enough to complete the tasks of fire control?
- Can ventilation be accomplished safely?
- Are the resources available to do the jobs?

DEFENSIVE FIRE ATTACK

A defensive fire attack is an exterior attack. When this type of attack is used, it is because existing conditions prohibit an offensive attack. A defensive attack employs large volumes of water to protect exposures (Figure 11.3). If adequate personnel and equipment are available, master streams can also be directed at the fire itself if burning hazardous materials are not a consideration.

The defensive operation is a heavy-duty attack that places emphasis on exposure protection and on stopping the spread of fire. The officer gives property up to the fire and determines where the fire department will stop the spread of fire.

At no time should an offensive attack and a defensive attack be conducted simultaneously. A safe fireground requires that a fire be fought from the inside or outside only. Trying to conduct both an offensive and a defensive attack is especially risky to the offensive team. Firefighters who are outside directing hose streams into a building may well injure or kill firefighters inside the structure.

WARNING
DO NOT CONDUCT SIMULTANEOUS OFFENSIVE AND DEFENSIVE FIRE ATTACKS. INJURY OR FATALITY MAY RESULT.

Figure 11.3 During the defensive attack, exposures become the main protection concern.

Following Standard Operating Procedures

After the attack modes have been defined and appropriate actions outlined for each mode, the fire department must compile and issue standard operating procedures (SOPs). A department that does not have written standard operating procedures does not have strategic plans. Such a department is only applying operational strategies and tactics. Of course, the company officer must be familiar with the department's standard operating procedures. There is no other way for the officer to make appropriate strategic decisions. Strategic plans are one of the few fire service topics that are almost entirely departmental, and must be learned as such. The officer must keep in mind that standard operating procedures are not detailed tactical guidelines, even though they describe preferred operating methods (Figure 11.4).

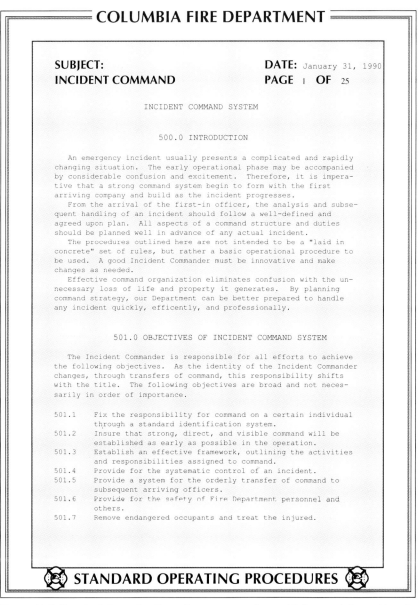

Figure 11.4 Standard Operating Procedures are excellent guidelines to follow; although, tactical guidelines must be determined at every incident.

When a standard operating procedure is issued, the strategic plan is well on its way to being developed. The next phase is to begin training companies to correctly apply the plans. Trial by fire is the true test, but any flaws in the strategic plan should be worked out in training. Training companies to employ standard operating procedures requires developing prescribed fireground evolutions, which should be included in the standard operating procedures. Each company member should be taught the correct methods of executing evolutions, and the company should perform drills as a group (Figure 11.5).

Training should begin at the officer level, then include firefighters. Multicompany drills are also necessary so companies can get accustomed to working as a team. These training exercises should also include the incident commander. Once the company has been trained to execute prescribed evolutions, they should be evaluated under simulated fireground conditions. The results provide information that can be used in the strategic planning phase.

Operating procedures should be continually reinforced with skull sessions using a chalkboard, dryboard, or overhead projector that simulates fire problems. The correct development of any strategic plan requires continuous input and modification. Departments that develop strategic plans and do not continue to improve and update them will eventually find their strategies out of date. A goal of the entire fire department should be to incorporate new information, equipment, and evolutions into standard operating procedures.

Figure 11.5 The company must practice drills as a team to perfect various fireground operations.

OPERATIONAL STRATEGIES AND TACTICS

Operational strategies and tactics are interrelated. Operational strategies are the actual plans needed to bring the situation under control. Tactics are the techniques or procedures used to implement the operational strategies (Figure 11.6 on next page). Examples of the more common operational strategies are:

- Rescue

- Exposure protection

- Confinement

- Extinguishment

- Ventilation

- Salvage

- Overhaul

Examples of some of the tactics used to implement these operational strategies are:

- Advancing handlines

- Cutting a hole in the roof

- Directing master streams on exposures

- Placing ladders

An example of the relationship between strategy and tactics would be rescuing a person from a second story window. Rescuing the person is the operational strategy; placing a ladder to execute the operational strategy is the tactic. Because many methods can be used to reach the same objective, tactics are often described in general terms.

When an incident occurs and the fire department is notified, the sequence moves into the operational strategy phase. The operational strategy phase is the portion of the sequence in which priorities are defined and evaluated. When the dispatcher receives the alarm, information is collected, and the company officer is able to choose the appropriate operational strategy using the following decision-making factors:

- Strategic plans (standard operating procedures)

- Standard fireground priorities

- Information obtained by the fire department

- The officer's experience

The strategic plans factor includes all information obtained while developing the strategic plans. This includes reports of previous incidents, pre-incident planning, fire prevention, and plans review.

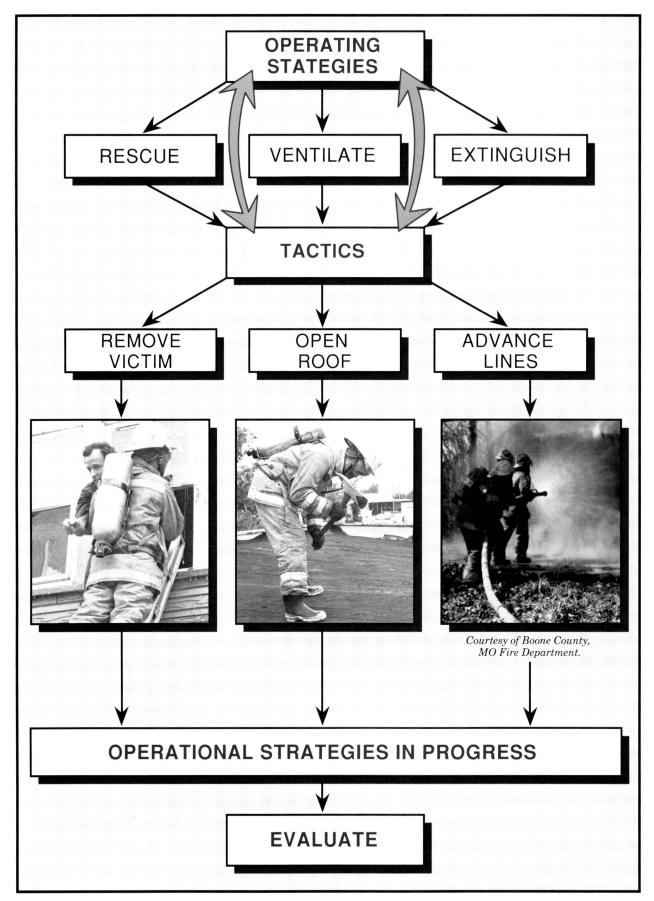

Figure 11.6 Operational strategies must be constantly evaluated while the tactical operations are in progress.

The standard fireground priorities are the order by which decisions are generally guided:

- Life safety
- Fire control
- Property conservation

Fireground decisions should be consistent with these priorities. Recognize, however, that the standard priorities do not necessarily dictate the *sequence* of fireground objectives. There are many cases when the best way to protect life is to put out the fire. In this case, extinguishment tactics would begin before rescue tactics. Conversely, letting hazardous materials burn is becoming increasingly acceptable due to the difficulty and expense of containing and recovering fire stream runoff. Many hazardous materials incidents are permitted to self-stabilize by allowing the products to burn off.

Priorities represent long-term goals and the sequence of fireground objectives represents the short-term objectives for reaching the goal. It may be necessary to temporarily give priority to a short-term objective like extinguishment or self-stabilization by burn-off to achieve the number one goal—life safety.

Information obtained by the fire department not only includes information compiled during the strategic planning phase, but, more important, is the information gained while sizing up the incident. The company officer, using strategic plans information, environmental information, dispatched information, and information gained visually during response, sizes up the specific situation. Size-up represents the bridge between strategic plans and operational strategy.

The fire officer's experience is a major consideration at any fire. Each officer has a pool of experience to call upon, and each officer will have a slightly different tactical concept from which to work while putting the operational strategy into action. Tactical decisions may be different, but the outcome should be consistent.

As the company officer enters the operational strategy phase, the initial task is to make a primary size-up of the incident. Usually, the company officer is the officer in charge of the incident, and he or she will make the primary size-up and choose the attack mode. The first arriving officer may maintain command throughout the incident; or, he or she may relinquish command if a higher authority arrives on the scene and officially assumes command.

For example, an engine and ladder company arrive at an incident. The company officer, in this case, is a lieutenant. When the chief arrives a few minutes later, the chief immediately determines the lieutenant has the situation under control and is satisfied with the lieutenant's appraisal of the situation. The chief permits the lieutenant to maintain command. Even though the chief out ranks the lieutenant, the lieutenant maintains command in this situation because the chief did not *officially* assume command from the lieutenant.

After selecting the attack mode, the officer in charge makes an initial report so everyone involved can make decisions consistent with the mode selected. The company officer must try to make an initial report as soon as possible after reaching the scene.

As the attack mode is implemented, the officer in charge begins a secondary size-up, quickly reviewing old and new information to assess: (Figure 11.7)

- The facts of the situation
- The probabilities of the situation
- The capabilities of the department

Figure 11.7 After tactical operations are in progress, the company officer should begin the secondary size-up.

After reviewing these factors, the officer should be able to assign priorities to the operational strategies. Once these priorities have been tentatively set, each objective must undergo a sequence evaluation. This evaluation is required because actions on the fireground are not broken into neat little blocks, but occur simultaneously. The officer in charge must evaluate each of the operational strategies selected to determine:

- The allotted resources
- The timing necessary with other objectives
- The sector priority
- The necessary communication process

After assessing the sequence of operational strategies, the officer in charge must quickly decide whether the primary size-up was correct. To make this check, the most important consideration is whether there are adequate resources on the scene to implement the operational strategies outlined (Figure 11.8). If there are not adequate resources, additional alarms might be sounded and the operational strategy or even the attack mode altered.

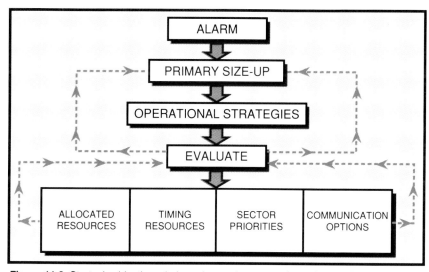

Figure 11.8 Strategic objectives during primary size-up are dependent on the simultaneous evaluation of these four variables.

THE TACTICAL STAGE

After finishing the operational strategy phase, the officer enters the tactical stage. In the tactical stage, the operational strategy is translated into action.

This phase begins with a command statement. There are six basic elements that must be communicated by the incident commander in a command statement:

- Command
- Tactical assignments

- Resource allocation
- Timetable
- Sector assignments
- Communication methods

Command assignment is a critical factor in the early stages of incident control. The company officer must accept "command" at this point or assign it to someone else so all units know who is in charge. The tactical assignments are made to specific companies within the guidelines provided for proper communications. The assignments include the resources, timetables, communication methods, and sector assignments.

After the assignments are made, the officer in charge must continue to monitor the situation. If the situation changes, the officer in charge may need to choose different operational strategies. If the operational strategies have not been met, or they have been met but this did not improve the situation, the officer may need to size up the situation again (Figure 11.9). If necessary, the attack mode, the operational strategies, and tactics can be changed as needed.

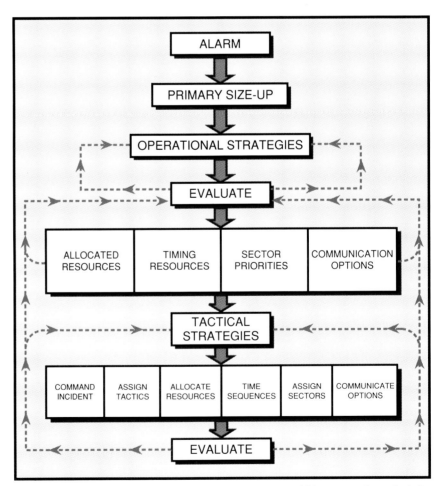

Figure 11.9 Strategic operations and tactical operations should be constantly evaluated.

SUMMARY

As the first commander at a scene, the company officer must be aware of the proper procedures for fireground management. The company officers should know the basis for strategic plans, operational strategies, and tactics. Strategic plans are the broad objectives of the department. They are developed using information gathered before an incident occurs and should be incorporated into the standard operating procedures. Operational strategies are the actual fireground mission and are based on strategic plans, size-up, and the officer's experience. Tactics are the actual processes used to arrive at the operational strategy. The company officer should know when to implement the different operational strategies and what tactics should be used to obtain the operational strategy. All three of these factors are varying. If the situations of the fire change, the officer may need to implement different strategic plans, operational strategies, and tactics in order to deal with the new situation.

SUPPLEMENTAL READINGS

Brunacini, Alan V. *Fire Command.* Quincy: National Fire Protection Association, 1985.

Clark, William E. *Fire Fighting: Principles & Practices.* New York: Dun·Donnelley Publishing Corporation, 1974.

Incident Command System. Stillwater, Okla.: Fire Protection Publications, Oklahoma State University, 1983.

Management in the Fire Service. Didactic Systems, Inc. Boston: National Fire Protection Association, 1977.

Size-Up

12

LESSON OBJECTIVES

After completing this chapter and related *Student Guide* applications, company officer candidates should be able to:

- Recognize the definition of *size-up*.

- Recognize the purposes of size-up.

- Recognize the major considerations in size-up.

- Recall the definition of *occupancy*.

- Discuss structural features that should be evaluated during size-up.

- Recall the basic resources available to the company officer during size-up.

- Explain the relationship between available resources and sizing up the incident.

- Demonstrate the ability to size up an emergency situation.

This chapter addresses NFPA 1021,
Standard Fire Officer Professional Qualifications (1987):
2-10.1
2-10.9
2-13.3.

Chapter 12
Size-Up

Size-up is a process of gathering and evaluating information, probabilities, and resources of a situation. It is the assessment of the incident during specific intervals and situations.

Loyd Layman, a noted fire service author, used the term size-up to describe the process of evaluating an incident in order to determine which course of action to pursue. Upon evaluation of all pertinent information, the company officer determines the strategy and the tactics to be used when developing plans to command the incident.

Size-up can be thought of as a spiral slowly converging on the correct tactics. Alarm information initially is sparse. Often, the address is the only information the officer receives. As the situation progresses, the company officer uses additional radio information, pre-incident plans, knowledge of previous incidents, and information obtained during response to tighten the spiral. Four basic areas of information must be considered:

- Environment
- Nature of incident
- Occupancy
- Resources

In each of these areas, the officer should strive to first determine the facts of the situation; second, the possibilities of the situation; and third, the probabilities of the situation (Figure 12.1 on next page).

ENVIRONMENTAL CONSIDERATIONS

Environmental factors affect the ability of the fire department to handle a situation. Current conditions will have an effect on types of emergency situations. Temperature extremes reduce

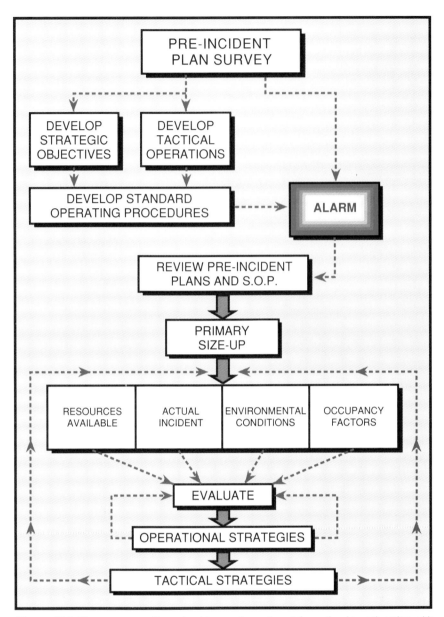

Figure 12.1 The company officer should use all previous information in conjunction with new information as it is made available to plan strategic and tactical operations during the incident.

performance of firefighters, high winds can cause fires to spread faster and spread the vapors of a hazardous materials incident, and topographic characteristics and precipitation can reduce response times.

Wind has an equal effect on both the incident and on fire department personnel. In cold weather, even a moderate wind will greatly reduce the ability of firefighters to function. Wind can also affect the severity of an incident. Toxic vapors from a hazardous materials incident can spread by wind (Figure 12.2). If the vapors are moving toward populated areas, consider calling more personnel to help with any possible evacuations. Wind coupled with dry conditions can cause a minor brush fire to grow into a major wildfire. Wind can also increase or decrease exposure

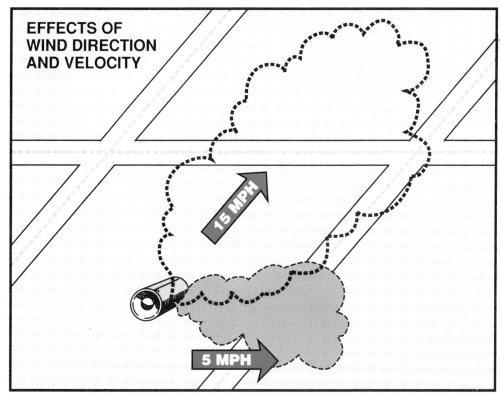

EFFECTS OF WIND DIRECTION AND VELOCITY

15 MPH

5 MPH

Figure 12.2 Wind direction and velocity are important considerations during primary size-up of incidents.

problems and affect ventilation of a structure. In windy situations, cross ventilation can be more effective; therefore, less personnel will be needed for ventilation assignments.

High winds, a major factor in several fires throughout history, should remind officers to consider master stream appliances for exposure protection as an initial priority and to use smoothbore tips instead of fog nozzles. Aerial equipment should be deployed to knock down firebrands even before the fire is ventilated or ventilates itself. In garden apartment fires, especially those involving shake or shingle roofs, aerial streams can be directed to protect adjacent roofs even some distance from the fire scene. Additional alarms can be sounded for aerial equipment if it looks like a fire is going to extend through the roof. It is easier to cancel additional alarms than to stop a fast-moving fire in high winds. Expect the unexpected.

Precipitation is always a factor when responding to or fighting fires. Wet conditions increase response times, and snow and ice will slow the response even more. In such instances, the company officer should expect a fire to progress farther before the first units arrive than if conditions were dry. Precipitation will also affect the ability of firefighters to perform. Relief will be needed sooner in wet conditions, especially during cold, wet conditions. Dry conditions will permit more severe ground cover and wooden shake or shingle fires. Extra companies may be needed in dry conditions that would not be required normally.

Weather will have many other effects on incident operations. In general, the company officer must ask three basic questions when sizing up weather:

- How will weather affect the ability of the firefighters to function?

- How will weather affect the incident?

- How will weather affect apparatus and other equipment?

Weather factors can be sized up very early in the incident sequence and generally during the response. The company officer should watch weather reports to know what to expect during the shift. On duty, the company officer must monitor the weather and anticipate any changes that might adversely affect operations.

Time of day is another obvious variable the company officer must consider. The dispatcher should give the time with the initial dispatch information on all alarms. After a firefighter has been asleep, it is difficult to tell if one hour or six hours have passed. Because loss of life is highest between midnight and 6 a.m., it is important for the officer to have an accurate idea of the time. Different time periods will also affect response time. Periods that affect response are the hour the taverns close, heavy rush hour traffic periods, and peak shopping times.

Topography is an important environmental consideration and can affect both fire spread and response time. Terrain and type of ground cover will affect the spread of wildfires. Roads and other natural barriers serve as good access points to cut off the spread of wildfires. Factors that affect response time are terrain, rivers and lakes, railroad tracks, and road conditions (Figure 12.3). Two questions the company officer must ask are: how will the topography affect the situation and how will it affect response time? The IFSTA validated **Hazardous Materials for First Responders** provides additional details on physical characteristics of terrain considerations.

Figure 12.3 Rough roads can hamper apparatus travel, especially if these roads are wet or icy.

NATURE OF THE INCIDENT

The nature of the incident obviously is important to the company officer because fire departments must handle a wide variety of incidents. The officer should determine the nature of the incident as soon as possible. If known, it should be included in the initial dispatch.

As the company officer determines the nature of the incident, the needs of the situation should become apparent: how many personnel will be required, what tools will be needed, what personal protection is necessary, and which other agencies should be notified. Experience should help the officer know what to expect.

Knowing the nature of the situation will also help the officer mentally outline the possibilities of the incident. During response, the officer can mentally map out priorities for the worst possibilities. These priorities can be modified on the scene, but with this method there is less chance of forgetting important details.

THE OCCUPANCY

The term occupancy refers to the specific building or facility under consideration. Another important term is *use,* which refers to the activities performed in the structure, the contents, or defines the use of the area.

The company officer should be familiar with special process hazards and hazardous materials used in the jurisdiction and their general life safety factors. The more potential victims, the more emergency personnel will be needed. The officer should know the number of potential occupants on both day and evening shifts from pre-incident plan data. The officer will not always be able to know the contents of an occupancy; therefore, he or she must determine complete information about it before an emergency occurs.

How an occupancy is used usually determines the probable contents. In such instances, assume the worst will happen. While evaluating the construction of the structure, the company officer will define many other incident scene determinants. Knowing the height and size of the building should give the company officer an idea of what resources are necessary. The officer should have a basic knowledge of buildings within the district, including:

- Height
- Age
- Construction materials
- Types of construction
- Modifications
- Roof design and type of covering

These items will tell a fire officer much about the probability of collapse, that, in some situations may be the most important factor in the size-up. Older buildings sometimes have cast-iron ornamental facades that often separate and fall during a fire. Other older buildings may be tied together to keep walls from separating. The officer should check the walls for ornamental metal stars that indicate this construction technique. The rods or cables between the stars can fail at moderate temperatures and the walls may collapse.

During an incident, the company officer must remain alert to potential building collapse. Some of the more obvious signs of instability are age, leaning or bulging walls, wall cracks, and smoking mortar joints. Note outside attachments, such as awnings, neon signs, and theater marquees (Figure 12.4). After heavy interior fire has been present for some time, the possibility of collapse must be considered.

Other structural factors the company officer must know about are egress paths and ventilation characteristics. The officer must mentally map out interior hallways and stairwells to assess life safety and line placement priorities.

The type of doors and windows also must be noted. This information will be important should forced entry or rescue become a major objective. It is also imperative that any special security measures the occupancy may employ be noted. These measures could include ornamental iron doors or windows, special locking devices, alarms, or guard dogs (Figure 12.5). For further discussion of these topics, see the IFSTA validated **Forcible Entry** manual.

Figure 12.4 Overhanging structures, such as movie theater marquees, pose a potential hazard during a fire.

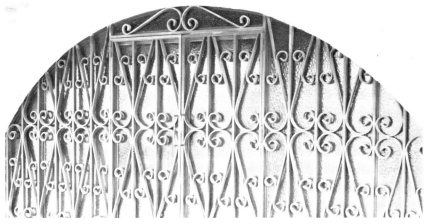

Figure 12.5 Ornamental iron doors and windows are becoming increasingly popular security devices that pose additional problems during an incident.

Ventilation characteristics include the location of such internal structural shafts as elevators, dumbwaiters, and light wells; mechanical ventilation equipment and systems; and easily vented roof fixtures such as skylights. The presence of such features can reduce department resources needed for ventilation. Remember, however, that such construction features may also permit the fire to travel through the structure virtually unchecked.

The occupancy's roof construction will be another factor affecting the officer's tactics (Figure 12.6). If the roof is determined to be unsafe, avoid placing firefighters inside the structure for interior attacks or on the roof for ventilation.

The company officer must also be aware of any built-in fire protection equipment and use any sprinklers or standpipe systems available. Supplementing a sprinkler system or using a standpipe will reduce the number of personnel needed to fight the fire.

Figure 12.6 Ventilation should be attempted only if the roof is safe.

RESOURCES

Resources include fire department equipment, personnel and administration, services available from mutual aid pacts, other city departments, and technical experts. The company officer must learn what resources are available on each alarm and through special alarms or requests.

The officer will use alarms to obtain the following four basic resources:

- Personnel
- Equipment
- Technical experts
- Extinguishing agents

Alarm assignments should be defined in the standard operating procedures. Each company officer dispatched to an incident should know all units assigned to an alarm by communications. The officer should be familiar enough with the department to know what equipment is being carried on each unit and how many officers and firefighters will respond.

If the officer arrives on the scene and finds a special process or problem, technical assistance should be summoned (Figure 12.7). Larger departments will employ fire protection engineers or administrative personnel well versed in building construction,

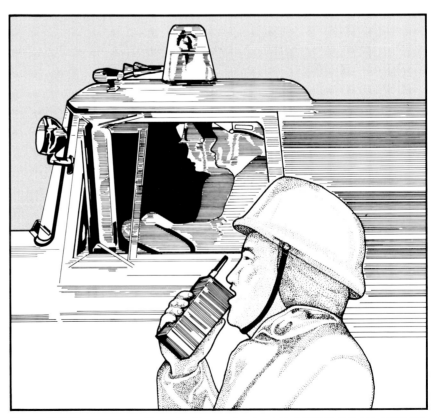

Figure 12.7 The company officer should use all resources available that can assist the operational strategy during an incident.

private fire protection equipment, process hazards, hazardous materials, and other technical problems. Often, fire prevention inspectors who have inspected an occupancy are valuable on the fireground because of their knowledge of the building. Smaller departments without such technical assistance look to other city departments or private firms for assistance. Information about technical sources should be included in pre-incident plans.

Personnel requirements are closely tied to the amount of extinguishing agent to be applied. The essence of extinguishing agent size-up is estimating how much water or extinguishing agent is needed for a proposed tactic and then determining if the equipment and personnel are available to apply it. If not, additional alarms must be called or the tactic changed.

> **ADDITIONAL ALARMS**
> **IF THERE IS A POSSIBLE NEED — BY THE TIME THE**
> **NEED IS OBVIOUS, IT MAY BE TOO LATE.**

SUMMARY

Size-up is used by the company officer to evaluate a situation and to judge the possible outcomes of the situation. Factors to be considered in sizing up an incident are the environment, the nature of the incident, the occupancy of the location, and the resources available. These factors can affect fire spread, hazards to life, response time, and the ability of firefighters to perform. Company officers should mentally evaluate all of these factors when responding to an incident. This will help them anticipate what might happen and give them the advantage when controlling the situation.

SUPPLEMENTAL READINGS

Clark, William E. *Fire Fighting: Principles & Practices.* New York: Dun·Donnelley Publishing Corporation, 1974.

Incident Command System. Stillwater, Okla.: Fire Protection Publications, Oklahoma State University, 1983.

Management in the Fire Service. Didactic Systems, Inc. Boston: National Fire Protection Association, 1977.

13

Incident Command
And Communications

LESSON OBJECTIVES

After completing this chapter and related *Student Guide* applications, company officer candidates should be able to:

- Distinguish between incident command and incident communications.

- Recognize common criteria for incident command procedures.

- Recall the major objectives of establishing incident communications procedures.

- Distinguish among direct and indirect orders, requests, and directives used at the incident site.

- Recognize the five C's of effective emergency communications.

- Demonstrate the ability to
  —Assign incident command duties.
  —Transmit effective emergency incident radio communications.

This chapter addresses NPFA 1021,
Standard for Fire Officer Professional Qualifications (1981):
2-5.4
2-10.1.

Chapter 13
Incident Command And Communications

The effective company officer must be able to size up a situation and determine a correct course of action. Many times the success of the entire operation will be based on sound judgment in establishing command and effective communication during the incident. Misunderstandings at this phase of an operation can be, and often are, devastating.

Emergency scene management methods must be defined in the standard operating procedures. Command and communications may be addressed in separate sections of the standard operating procedures, but the company officer must relate to them when doing every incident analysis.

An incident command system will define how the chain of authority forms and progresses during an incident. Most important, command definition should establish the authority for first-arriving units to assume command. It should also be made clear *who* in the first-arriving units is to assume control of the incident. Command definition must also establish procedures for transferring command.

In his book, *Fire Command,* Chief Alan Brunacini discusses the method of command used in Phoenix, Arizona. This procedure has earned wide acceptance in the fire service. Different variations of command procedures have been developed and successfully implemented in other areas. All effective procedures meet eight common criteria:

- Organizational structure is defined.
- Unity of command is maintained.
- Span of control is not exceeded.
- Division of labor is used.
- Discipline is required of everyone on the fireground.

- Fundamental group principles are incorporated.
- Authority to establish command at any level is explicitly stated.
- Procedures for effectively transferring command are outlined.

Close examination of these criteria reveal that no well-guarded secrets have been discovered. The simple truth is that effective command is the application of sound management skills to a fireground operation. These are the same management skills that the company officer uses in the station; only the objectives differ. Many company officers excuse their failure to manage at an incident scene by contending the urgency of the situation merited violation of management principles. There are two flaws in this argument. First, an incident to which the fire department is called is not an emergency to the well-trained officer. Such a situation requires swift action, something the company officer does on a professional basis. Second, if the incident deteriorates or is too large for a single department to handle, the most valuable tool available is management skill. Discarding this tool at the fireground is like an airline pilot throwing the control stick out the window of a disabled aircraft to lighten the load.

Communication management methods define the procedure and language to be used at the incident scene. By including communications in the standard operating procedures, much confusion can be eliminated at the incident scene. The communications procedure must do two things:

- Establish the use of specific common terms that mean the same thing to all fire personnel.
- Establish a system of transmitting periodic progress reports to keep all units current on the progress of the incident.

The specific language commonly lists terms that should be used in preference to all other synonyms. For instance, *residence* might always be used to describe the living quarters of a family instead of the words home, house, dwelling, or one-family dwellings. Then each time the word residence is used, everyone involved understands its meaning. Many fire departments are switching to clear language instead of the 10-codes that have been used over the radio for a generation.

RADIO COMMUNICATIONS

The purpose of fire department radio communications is to tie all of the elements of the organization together so that each element can perform its task in an efficient, informed manner. Radio equipment is designed to provide a method of transmitting and receiving critical or pertinent tactical information to or from other field units, the communications center, or the incident commander. This information can be task-related (Engine 7 to Command; we need an additional supply line to support Truck 37's ladder pipe) or the information can be a direct order based upon the decision of the incident commander (Command to Alarm: Transmit third alarm. All companies to report to staging).

Individuals who operate radio equipment should realize that all radio transmissions can be monitored by the news media and the public. Any communications that are transmitted via radio could very well be repeated on tomorrow's front page. Radio operators should always be aware of what they are saying, and never transmit a message that may bring liability or embarrassment to the department.

Basic Radio Communications

Telling a rookie firefighter, "Push this button and tell them what you need," is not an effective method of training personnel to use fire department radios. Radio training is not strictly related to verbiage; it relates to the total communications spectrum (Figure 13.1). Some of the areas that the company officer should be aware of are

- Basic radio operation and maintenance
- Radio frequency assignments and usage
- Departmental radio procedures

Figure 13.1 Every member of the company should be trained to use proper radio communication techniques.

TRANSMISSION OF ESSENTIAL INFORMATION

An additional but often forgotten factor when transmitting information and orders via radio is that *only essential information* should be transmitted. For example, consider the difference in the following two radio communications:

Radio Communication 1:
"This is Lieutenant Thompson on Engine 57 portable. I need another truck company at Box 1333 for manpower."

Radio Communication 2:
"Engine 57 portable to communications— Dispatch 1 truck company to Box 1333."

In Radio Communication 1, it serves absolutely no purpose to identify oneself by name. "Engine 57 portable" communicates to the dispatcher that the company officer is requesting the truck company. In addition, the use of "I need another" and "at this location" waste radio air time, which is critical during most incidents. Furthermore, communicating "for manpower" is not necessary. The company officer does not provide the reason or justification for requests over the air. He or she simply transmits the request.

Note that Radio Communication 2 required only 12 words. Although brevity is of the utmost importance, this is only part of the advantage of this transmission. Note that it communicates the request in a concise, clear manner. The dispatcher relays the request to the appropriate source. Chances of error or miscommunication are significantly reduced.

Direct Orders

An example of a direct order is, "Smith, ventilate the roof." Direct orders are often used in fire and emergency situations to deploy personnel and sometimes en route conditions. A direct order can be made more explicit by adding extra information such as who is to carry out the task and why, how, when, and where it must be done. The company officer must judge how specific to make the order by considering the urgency of the task and the capabilities of the individual given the directive.

Company officers must display confidence when giving a direct command, but temper their judgment with the amount of specific information they include in their order. They should also realize they are giving a directive to a trained individual to perform a certain task, at a certain time, and most important, within that individual's ability and training.

An order such as, "Smith, get a roof ladder and a flat-head axe, then ventilate the structure by cutting a hole in the top of the roof where you see the smoke rising from the eaves," is not only a waste of time, but is also an insult to a seasoned firefighter (Figure 13.2). If it is necessary to be that explicit, the firefighter is being ordered to perform a task beyond his or her capability. The firefighter might suffer an injury or pose a hazard to other firefighters. Select and order personnel wisely.

Figure 13.2 Excessive detail when giving an order can insult and belittle a seasoned firefighter.

Requests Or Indirect Orders And Directives

A request is a milder way of giving a verbal order or directive but has almost the same effect as a direct order. For example, "Williams, would you please help Mike wash the rig?" is a request that serves as a directive. Requests are appropriate at the fire station but not, as a rule, at fires or emergencies.

The real problem with a request is that it implies that the subordinate has a choice. Even though the subordinate will usually act in a manner the officer desires, the officer will be displeased if the subordinate chooses to do otherwise. As a rule, therefore, requests should not be used unless the officer is ready to accept the results of the subordinate's decision.

Indirect orders or directives can be even weaker than requests. An officer who says to a firefighter, "the wheels are dirty," expects the firefighter to take the initiative and clean the wheels. The drawback with an implied directive is that the firefighter may not understand the message and the work may not get done. An implied directive is best used with experienced personnel or personnel whose initiative is developing.

At the incident scene, there is no time for the company officer to think about the correct method of communicating. Therefore, the company officer must incorporate good communications procedures into everyday operations until these skills become second nature. There are five "C's" of communication that every company officer must master:

- Conciseness
- Clarity
- Confidence
- Control
- Capability

Conciseness

Many functions must be performed at an incident scene, and most will be accompanied by some form of communication. Therefore, communications must be kept as concise as possible or there will not be enough time to transmit every message. To ensure conciseness, the company officer must learn to plan communications. This can be done by planning the message. The officer should:

- Make messages task oriented.
- Direct messages to companies, not individuals.
- Match the message to the receiver.
- Keep messages specific.
- Eliminate options from messages.

Clarity

The clarity of a message will add to the overall effectiveness of all incident operations. The officer must use standard terms and everyday language when possible. The officer should also strive to combine clarity with simplicity.

To remain simple, good orders should communicate only one task at a time and have the unit report back for further tasks. Consecutive orders to different units must be well spaced to avoid any question that separate orders are being transmitted. Orders should be transmitted in a timely fashion. Many operations can be anticipated by an experienced incident commander, but the order assigning units to those operations should not be issued until those operations are to be undertaken.

Confidence

To control the incident, the incident commander must show confidence when using communication equipment. When confidence is communicated, receiving units react with confidence. The incident commander can begin communicating confidence by using a calm, natural tone and by speaking at a controlled rate.

Control

Communications will rapidly break down if they are not managed. The two most important persons involved in controlling communications on the company level are the dispatcher and the officer in charge (Figure 13.3).

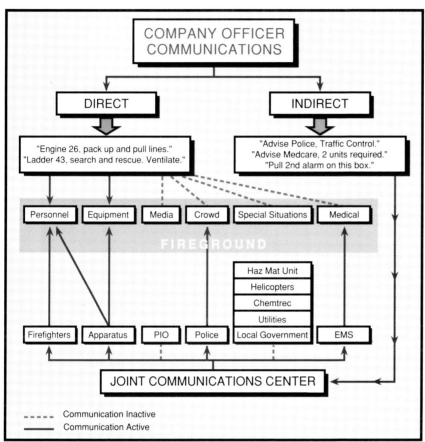

Figure 13.3 The company officer has direct and indirect communication options on the fireground.

Everyone on the fireground should follow two rules to control communications. First, units must identify themselves in every transmission, as outlined in the standard operating procedures. Second, the receiver must acknowledge every message by repeating the essence of the message to the sender.

Engine 4:
"Engine 4—Communications. We are on the scene and have a dumpster fire. We will handle. Cancel all other units."

Communications:
"Communications— Engine 4. Understand this is a dumpster fire and you will handle. Other dispatched units...."

Requiring the receiver to acknowledge every message ensures that everyone understands the same terms. This acknowledgement is much like the communications cycle discussed in Chapter 3 with the receiver repeating the message to the sender. This feedback tells the sender the message was understood as transmitted, or it notifies the sender that the message was not understood and further clarification is necessary.

Capability

The communication process hinges on capable message senders and receivers. Capability not only implies proficiency; it implies willingness to communicate. The company officer must be willing to give orders and to listen. It also implies that the company officer is able to give a higher priority to communication and responsibility than to personal interests.

SUMMARY

Organization on the fireground is dependent on proper use of command and communications. Command defines how the chain of command will develop on the fireground and communication ties the chain together. Effective fireground communications depend upon everyone involved understanding the messages being transmitted. Messages that are brief, impersonal, and to the point are much easier to understand. Procedures for both fireground command and radio communication should be set forth in a department's standard operating procedures.

SUPPLEMENTAL READINGS

Brunacini, Alan V. *Fire Command*. Quincy: National Fire Protection Association, 1985.

Clark, William E. *Fire Fighting: Principles & Practices*. New York: Dun·Donnelley Publishing Corporation, 1974.

The Fire Chief's Handbook. Ed. James F. Casey. 4th ed. New York: Technical Publishing Company, 1978.

Incident Command System. Stillwater, Okla.: Fire Protection Publications, Oklahoma State University, 1983.

Management in the Fire Service. Didactic Systems, Inc. Boston: National Fire Protection Association, 1977.

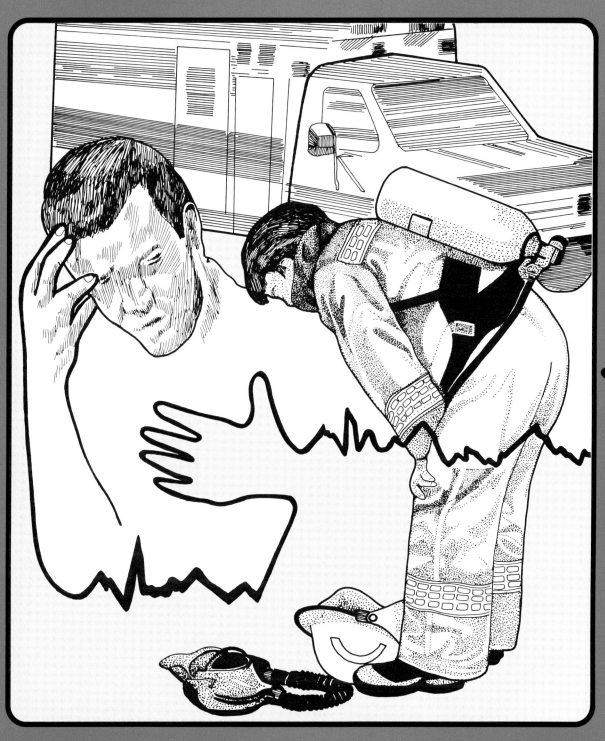

Firefighter Safety
And Health

LESSON OBJECTIVES

After completing this chapter and related *Student Guide* applications, company officer candidates should be able to:

- Recognize elements of NFPA Standard 1500 for which the company officer is directly responsible.

- Recall the most frequent causes of injuries and fatalities among potentially hazardous conditions that could cause injury or death to firefighters.

- Discuss actions the company officer can take to reduce firefighter injuries.

- Recall definitions of *acute stress* and *chronic stress*.

- Recognize the stages of chronic stress.

- Recognize physical, environmental, and psychological stressors.

- Recognize the signs of psychological stress.

- Discuss guidelines for handling company members who may be substance abusers.

- Recognize types of situations that commonly cause critical incident stress.

- Recognize symptoms of critical incident stress.

- Explain the purpose of each of the components of a posttrauma program.

- Explain the purpose of a wellness program.

- Demonstrate the ability to counsel firefighters in methods of stress reduction.

- Investigate and analyze company time-loss injuries.

This chapter addresses NFPA 1021,
Standard for Fire Officer Professional Qualifications (1987):

2-2.6	4-7.3.
2-3.1	
2-12.1	
2-12.2	
2-12.4	

Chapter 14
Firefighter Safety And Health

Because of their position in the organizational structure, company officers have a responsibility for each firefighter under their command. This responsibility requires that the officer be aware of the various safety factors that threaten the performance and well-being of both the company as a team and its individual members.

Company officers must develop the skills necessary to manage the responsibility of company safety. In addition to having these skills, the company officer must have the ability and knowledge to correct situations that are hazardous to firefighters. It is imperative that conditions that might threaten the safety of the company be detected before an incident occurs that results in the injury or death of a firefighter.

FIREFIGHTER INJURIES

Injuries are a serious risk in fire fighting. In the late 1980s, approximately 102,000 firefighter injuries were reported per year. These injuries included outpatient care as well as admissions to hospitals. Many injuries can be prevented by effective supervision and training, proper use of personal protective equipment, and higher levels of physical fitness for firefighters. A good physical fitness program serves the firefighter in many ways; for example, physically fit firefighters are less likely to suffer strains and sprains, which account for over 30 percent of all firefighter injuries. Physical exercise is also very effective in reducing stress.

In 1987, the National Fire Protection Association Standards Council issued NFPA 1500, *Standard on Fire Department Occupational Safety and Health*. The objective of this standard is to reduce the number and severity of firefighter injuries. The company officer has the responsibility of supervising firefighters to ensure that the guidelines set forth in this standard are met. These guidelines include:

- Inspection, maintenance, and repair of vehicles
- Properly worn and maintained protective clothing
- Proper use and maintenance of SCBA
- Proper use and maintenance of PASS devices
- Fire station safety
- Proper apparatus riding procedures

These are only a few of the guidelines set forth in NFPA 1500. Company officers are responsible for reviewing the entire standard and determining which aspects of the standard come under their direct supervision (Figure 14.1).

Figure 14.1 Company officers should ensure the safety of the personnel under their command.

Sources Of Injuries

Many serious injuries occur on the fireground. It is estimated that 55 percent of all firefighter injuries occur on the scene of an incident. Other areas of injury include approximately 15 percent nonemergency incidents, 5 percent during training, 5 percent while responding to or returning from an incident, and the remaining 20 percent occur in various activities while on duty.

The National Fire Protection Association conducts an annual survey of accident locations and injury types. Table 14.1 illustrates the injuries by nature and the type of duty that were reported for 1987. The next aspect to examine is the cause of

TABLE 14.1
FIRE FIGHTER INJURIES BY NATURE OF INJURY AND TYPE OF DUTY

Nature of injury	Responding to or returning from an incident No.	%	Fire ground emergency No.	%	Nonfire No.	%	Training No.	%	Other on-duty No.	%	Total No.	%
Burns (fire or chemical)	-	-	5,770	10.0	170	1.2	510	8.4	385	1.9	6,835	6.6
Smoke or gas inhalation	-	-	8,040	13.9	345	2.5	155	2.6	165	.8	8,705	8.5
Eye irritation	235	4.6	4,905	8.5	350	2.5	330	5.4	810	4.1	6,630	6.4
Wound, cut, bleeding, bruise	1,395	27.5	13,200	22.9	3,075	22.0	1,490	24.5	5,260	26.6	24,420	23.8
Dislocation, fracture	315	6.2	1,570	2.7	320	2.3	295	4.9	750	3.8	3,250	3.2
Heart attack or stroke	65	1.3	240	.4	60	.4	60	1.0	255	1.3	680	.7
Strain, sprain	2,520	49.7	16,565	28.7	6,140	44.0	2,605	42.8	9,300	47.1	37,130	36.2
Frostbite	20	.4	185	.3	35	.3	25	.4	10	.1	275	.3
Heat exhaustion	115	2.3	4,075	7.1	120	.9	235	3.9	140	.7	4,685	4.6
Other	410	8.0	3,205	5.5	3,325	23.9	370	6.1	2,680	13.6	9,990	9.7
	5,075		57,755		13,940		6,075		19,755		102,600	

Reprinted with permission from *Fire Command,* (Vol. 55 No. 11) Copyright 1988, National Fire Protection Association, Quincy, MA. 02269.

injuries in the largest category—the fireground. Annual reports continually support an approximate breakdown of causes of injuries on the fireground. The major causes of fireground injuries are shown in Figure 14.2.

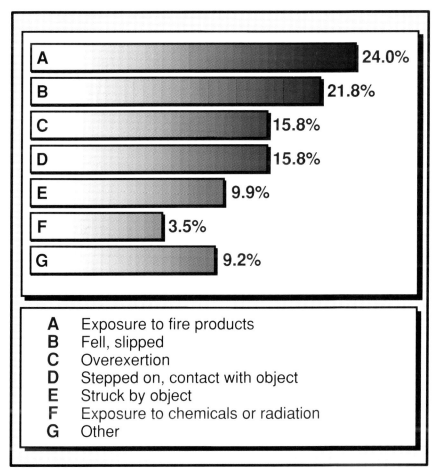

A	Exposure to fire products
B	Fell, slipped
C	Overexertion
D	Stepped on, contact with object
E	Struck by object
F	Exposure to chemicals or radiation
G	Other

Figure 14.2 Firefighter fireground injuries for 1987. Data reprinted with permission from *Fire Command,* (Vol.55 No. 11) Copyright © 1988, National Fire Protection Association, Quincy, MA 02269.

By knowing the injuries that occur, where they occur, and the causes, a method can be developed to recognize, reduce, and eliminate factors that could injure firefighters in the course of their duties.

Several actions by the company officer will have positive effects in reducing a substantial number of firefighter injuries. These measures include:

- Personal commitment by the company officer to reduce injuries

- Enforcing a policy requiring the use of *all* personal protective equipment by every firefighter and company officer

- Designing and conducting effective training for firefighters in the high hazard areas including
  —Use of self-contained breathing apparatus
  —Recognizing inherent hazards in fireground operations
  —Vehicle safety

- Developing and supporting effective physical fitness and weight control programs

- Conducting an objective and thorough investigation of time-loss injuries to determine
  —If unsafe acts are being performed (indicates need for training)
  —Existence of unsafe conditions
  —If equipment is inadequate or inappropriate for the task

STRESS

Stress is simply an adjustment to change. The change can be good or it can be bad. In psychology, good stress is called eustress and bad stress is called distress. Because distress is considered harmful, this chapter will only concern itself with this form of stress.

To some degree, stress is beneficial. When controlled, stress can help a firefighter perform more quickly and efficiently. Uncontrolled, stress can build to dangerous levels that affect a firefighter's health and ability to function. These adverse effects occur when the stressor, or demanding stimulus, is beyond the adjustment capability of the firefighter. (It is important to note that not all firefighters will adjust with the same effectiveness.)

Stress can be acute or chronic. Acute stress is short term, and chronic stress is of long duration. Current theory indicates that most forms of acute stress do not cause permanent damage. Chronic stress, on the other hand, can lead to permanent damage.

After examining Dr. Hans Selye's General Adaptation Syndrome (GAS), it may be easier to understand why chronic stress and not acute stress affects our health. Dr. Selye broke the

10-90

physiological response of a stressor into three distinct stages: (Figure 14.3)

Stage 1: Alarm reaction stage is the initial reaction to the stressor. The body responds with a massive release of hormones, including adrenaline. During this stage blood volume decreases.

Stage 2: The resistance stage has also been called the fight/ flight response. In this stage, the body prepares to defend itself or remove itself from the presence of the stressor. During this stage, the body may seem to be adapting quite nicely; however, energy needed to continue is being depleted. When the adaptational energy is gone, the body passes to the third and final stage.

Stage 3: The final stage is called the exhaustion stage. This is the stage where permanent damage to the system occurs. This damage may be small or large. It should be noted that if the stressor is not removed during this stage death will result.

Now it should be clear why chronic stress is a health concern. Simply stated, chronic stress has the ability to pass through all three of the GAS stages. A few of the health problems that have been linked to chronic stress are heart disease, ulcers, cancer, and insomnia.

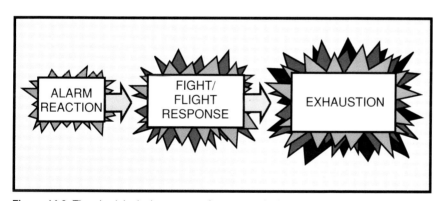

Figure 14.3 The physiological response of a stressor in three stages.

Physical, Environmental, And Psychological Stressors

The occupation of firefighter requires strenuous exertion, often in adverse weather conditions. Exertion is a physical stressor and weather is an environmental stressor. Psychological stressors are slightly more difficult to identify. Some psychological stressors associated with the profession of fire fighting are:

● The sound of the alarm

● Abrupt interruption of meals and sleep

● The unknown of responding to an alarm

● The unknown dangers while at a scene

All of these stressors have profound and damaging effects on the body, especially on the cardiovascular system.

In conjunction with severe environmental conditions of high and low temperatures are problems of high humidity, hazardous breathing atmospheres, and high noise levels. These all cause stress on the body and are capable of causing permanent injuries. For example, exposure to high temperature in humid conditions results in fatigue and will have adverse effects on the cardiovascular system (Figure 14.4).

Firefighters also are exposed to psychological stressors that are not exclusive to their profession. Some of these stressors are:

- Poor work relationships
- Poor work atmosphere
- Lack of promotions
- Lack of support or praise by superiors
- Difficult work roles

Psychological stressors from firefighters' personal lives can also affect their health and work performance. Some common sources of off-the-job stressors are divorce or separation, death or illness of a family member, and financial difficulties (Figure 14.5).

Figure 14.4 Environmental conditions can have adverse effects on the cardiovascular system and fatigue the firefighter. *Courtesy of David Wiist, Edmond Fire Department, Edmond, OK.*

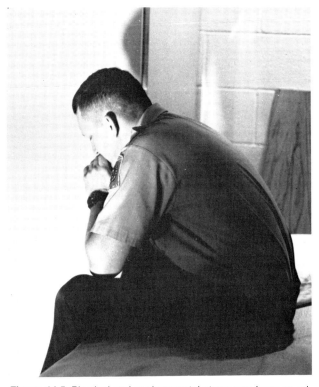

Figure 14.5 Physical and environmental stress can have an adverse effect on the firefighter and may lead to depression.

Reducing Physical And Environmental Stress

By supporting and enforcing sound safety and health care policies, the company officer can do a great deal to help maintain firefighters' health. Proper use of personal protective equipment will help reduce the effects of physical and environmental stressors. Positive-pressure self-contained breathing apparatus will provide clean air to breathe, and turnout clothing will protect the body from temperature extremes. A policy requiring training in, and the proper use of, personal protective equipment should be implemented and strictly enforced in every fire department.

In addition to use of protective clothing and equipment, company officers should enforce strict physical fitness programs. These programs are designed to reduce damaging effects of stress by increasing the functional capability of the cardiovascular system. There are other programs designed to decrease the risks associated with coronary heart disease and to reduce firefighter injuries in general (Figure 14.6). These programs include:

- Annual medical check-ups

- Weight control programs

- No smoking regulations

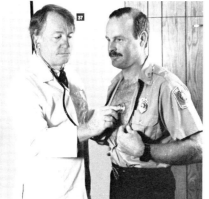  

Figure 14.6 Physical fitness programs are now a part of the modern fire service.

Psychological Stress—Signals and Reduction

The company officer has the responsibility of attempting to recognize when a firefighter may be under stress. Some of the more noticeable signs that indicate that stress may be building to dangerous levels are:

- General irritability

- Emotional instability

- Inability to concentrate

- Fatigue

- Insomnia and restless sleep

- Loss of appetite

- Alcohol and drug use

It is imperative to respond to any of these signs. In some cases, individuals may not realize they are showing signs of stress, and just pointing out their behavior may help identify a need for assistance. If the individual is indeed under a stressful situation, the company officer needs to be understanding (Figure 14.7). The firefighter may just need to talk to someone. This one-to-one communication is often the best medicine. If this method does not work, tell the individual that he or she might want to consider professional help and refer them to counseling services that are available to the fire department. It is important to convey genuine concern and understanding for their problem, and support for their decision to seek professional help. In situations where the firefighter refuses to seek help voluntarily, the company officer has the responsibility to insist that the firefighter seek help. In some situations, it may be necessary to make this a condition of employment.

Other common methods of stress reduction are:

- Getting adequate rest
- Regular exercise
- A balanced diet
- Taking a vacation
- Taking "quiet times"
- Laughter
- Relaxation or slowing down

Figure 14.7 If a firefighter needs to talk with someone, the company officer should take the time to listen.

Substance Abuse

Both alcohol and drug abuse are real problems in the fire service. High levels of stress, both on and off the job, may lead a person to alcohol or drugs as an escape. Work performance of an individual under the influence will be unpredictable. This person becomes unreliable and will eventually be unable to function as a firefighter.

Because of the investment made in training a firefighter, fire departments often cannot afford to fire an individual who is found to be a substance abuser. The firefighter should be relieved of duty while seeking professional assistance with the problem. Most medical insurance policies will pay for this type of treatment. The fire department will usually find that the investment of helping the firefighter will be well worth it.

It is less expensive to help a substance abuser overcome a habit than to fire the individual and have to hire and train someone new. The fire department will get a return on its investment when it can retain a trained and seasoned firefighter who is drug and alcohol free.

CRITICAL INCIDENT STRESS

A type of stress that deserves special attention is the stress that occurs as a result of a particularly traumatic or disturbing incident. This type of stress has been called "Critical Incident Stress" by Dr. Jeff Mitchell. Critical incident stress can be very detrimental to both a firefighter's career and to his or her personal life. Some of the incidents that commonly cause critical incident stress are:

- Multiple casualty incidents
- Incidents where people sustain injuries that cause extreme suffering and pain
- An incident in which another firefighter is killed or injured
- Incidents in which children are killed or injured
- A failed search and rescue operation that results in the death of the victim
- An incident in which death occurs despite a successful search and rescue operation

Not all firefighters will suffer from critical incident stress after responding to a major incident because different people react differently to the same situation. However, the majority of the firefighters who are involved with a critical incident will have some type of reaction. This reaction, called critical incident stress, is a normal response to an abnormal situation. Company officers should remember they cannot prevent critical incident stress. Critical incident stress is not preventable by anyone.

Symptoms Of Critical Incident Stress

There are many symptoms that indicate a firefighter may be suffering from critical incident stress. These symptoms can appear at the scene of the incident, or hours, days, weeks, or even months after the incident. Some of the more common symptoms are:

At the scene

- Denial of the situation (this can't be happening)
- Anger
- Doubts of performance ability
- Anxiety
- Frustration
- A sense of hopelessness

After the incident

- Feelings of guilt
- Restlessness
- Irritability
- Drug or alcohol abuse
- Sleep disturbances
- Flashbacks of the incident
- Decreased appetite

As previously stated, critical incident stress is not preventable; however, a company officer can do a great deal to prevent long-term effects of critical incident stress by relaying to the company that these symptoms are normal.

In cases of critical incident stress, one of the largest problems a fire department has is the image and history of the "macho" firefighter (Figure 14.8). A firefighter with this self-image can suffer guilt feelings when experiencing or showing any of the critical incident stress symptoms. Company officers, by doing away with this image, can relieve a great deal of additional stress-caused guilt feelings. There is no reason to feel guilty about experiencing critical incident stress symptoms. Company officers should remember that they themselves are not immune to critical incident stress or the feelings of guilt when experiencing the symptoms.

Company officers also should not feel guilty when faced with a company member who is suffering from critical incident stress. Remember, such feelings are not preventable. There are, however, several things the company officer can do to help alleviate the immediate reactions to a critical incident. One thing would be to request that the company be placed out of service for an hour or two. This will let the firefighters take their time getting the apparatus and themselves back in service and relieve some of the pressure they would feel rushing to get ready for the next call.

Figure 14.8 The day of the "Macho" firefighter image is archaic.

Making sure the company gets proper rest after the incident is one of the easiest ways to relieve stress. Another important item is to help the firefighters fulfill any special needs they may have as a result of the incident. Some of these needs may include a vacation or just someone with whom to discuss the trauma of the emergency (Figure 14.9).

Figure 14.9 Discussion among the company members can help relieve the trauma and stress associated with emergency responses.

Reducing Critical Incident Stress (A Posttrauma Program)

Critical incident stress can be very damaging to a firefighter and costly to a department. A good way to reduce the damage and cost is with a well planned and implemented posttrauma program. Such a program demands cooperation between the fire department and mental health practitioners. Like all other fire department programs, a posttrauma program must be carefully thought out and planned. A hastily assembled program can do more harm than good. An effective posttrauma program should include the following:

- Training
- Peer support
- Debriefing
- Counseling

TRAINING

The first step in reducing the effects of critical incident stress is to train firefighters about the psychological hazards of the job. This training session should include information about critical incident stress, including its causes, symptoms, and some effective coping techniques. It is important to remember that this type of training is different than normal fire fighting training and is not exclusive to entry level firefighters. All fire department personnel should be included in the critical incident training.

PEER SUPPORT

The purpose of peer support is to give a firefighter who has been exposed to a critical incident someone to talk to. Peer supporters are not mental health professionals; they are fire department personnel who have received special training in the area of critical incident stress (Figure 14.10). Peer supporters enable firefighters to talk to someone who will understand the situation the firefighter has faced. Peer supporters may also assist the mental health professionals during the debriefing stage.

Careful selection of a peer support team is critical. The most important characteristic of a potential peer supporter is the ability to keep information confidential. Other important aspects include:

- Personality—easy to talk to and well liked
- Openness
- Variety of departmental ranks
- Ability to follow through with a project

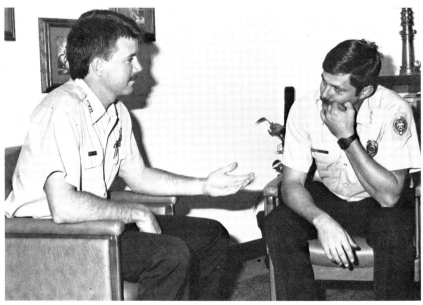

Figure 14.10 At times, fellow firefighters with special training help solve critical incident stress problems.

DEBRIEFING

Debriefing is the next phase in the posttrauma program. Debriefing is a formal meeting led by a mental health professional. Debriefings should take place within a few days of the incident. This meeting should be mandatory for personnel who were involved in the incident. A debriefing gives the firefighters a chance to share their feelings and to discover that other firefighters are having the same feelings and problems.

Debriefing teams should be composed of mental health professionals and specially trained fire department personnel. One of the most important tasks in forming a posttrauma program is the selection of the mental health professionals. It is essential that all mental health professionals who serve on debriefing teams have specific training in critical incident stress.

COUNSELING

Additional help is seldom needed after a good debriefing session. At times, however, firefighters will need some additional help in the form of counseling. Counseling is indicated when severe critical incident stress symptoms are reported. Another sign that counseling may be needed is excessive depression. The mental health professional in charge of the debriefing session usually will be the one to suggest additional help. In most instances, only a few sessions are needed.

If several company members are still experiencing severe stress following the initial debriefing, a follow-up debriefing session might be in order. Company officers should consult with the mental health professional who conducted the initial session to determine if this is necessary.

WELLNESS PROGRAMS

Wellness programs are a fairly new concept in the fire service. These programs are designed to provide for the occupational health needs of a fire department's most important resource—its personnel. Wellness programs should monitor and maintain records on firefighter health and fitness. These records should be confidential and include:

- Results of medical exams
- Results of physical fitness test
- Occupational illnesses
- Occupational injuries
- Possible exposure to hazardous materials
- Possible exposure to contagious diseases

The overall wellness program is composed of three subprograms:

- The medical program
- The physical fitness program
- The member assistance program

All medical tests and physical examinations are conducted as part of the medical program. The results of these tests are used to determine if a firefighter is physically capable of performing assigned duties. The physical fitness program is used to monitor and maintain the peak physical fitness of a department's personnel through rigorous exercise and weight training. Weight and exercise rooms should be provided and their use encouraged (Figure 14.11). The physical fitness program also helps personnel recover from occupational illnesses and injuries. The member assistance program identifies and assists members with problems resulting from stress, substance abuse, and personal matters. Such a program should be available to all fire department personnel and their families.

All aspects of the wellness program should be supervised by a fire department doctor. This doctor should have special training in the occupational safety and health problems faced by emergency personnel. It is the responsibility of the fire department doctor to advise and direct firefighters on health matters and to determine if they are capable of performing their assigned duties.

Figure 14.11 Weight and exercise rooms in the station encourage participation in wellness programs.

SUMMARY

There are many factors that influence firefighter injuries and health. Some of these are inherent dangers of the job. Others are controllable conditions that an alert officer can recognize and take action to correct. To do this, the company officer must be aware of all aspects of company safety. By realizing where accidents are occurring and what the major causes are, the company officer can take steps to prevent unnecessary injury and death and to teach firefighters to be more safety and health conscious.

Stress and substance abuse problems must be addressed immediately to preserve the health of the affected firefighter and to keep the fire fighting team intact. The "team effort" of fire fighting will eventually be sacrificed if a stress or substance abuse problem is not dealt with. The company officer who takes an active role in dealing with these problems will find that they are controllable and will be rewarded with an experienced, healthy fire fighting team.

SUPPLEMENTAL READINGS

Atkinson, Richard C., Rita L. Atkinson, and Ernest R. Hilgard. *Introduction to Psychology*. San Diego: Harcourt Brace Jovanovich, Inc., 1981.

Firefighter Occupational Safety. 1st ed. Stillwater, Okla.: Fire Protection Publications, Oklahoma State University, 1979.

Genest, Myles, and Sharon Genest. *Psychology and Health*. Champaign: Research Press, 1987.

Rosenham, David L., and Martin E.P. Seligman. *Abnormal Psychology*. New York: W.W. Norton and Company, 1984.

15

Company Officer's Liability

LESSON OBJECTIVES

After completing this chapter and related *Student Guide* applications, company officer candidates should be able to:

- Recognize the principles of administrative law.

- Distinguish the difference between legal duty and liability.

- Recall the definition of *tort liability*.

- Explain the essential components of tort liability.

- Recall the definitions of *negligence, standard of care, and causation.*

- Explain the company officer's responsibility for subordinates' acts.

- Recognize the elements of due process.

- Discuss the company officer's role in the affirmative action process.

This chapter addresses NFPA 1021,
Standard for Fire Officer Professional Qualifications (1987):
6-5.1
6-5.2.

Chapter 15
Company Officer's Liability

As a supervisor and as a fire department employee, the company officer's actions are influenced every day by a number of laws, ordinances, and regulations. One common misconception regarding the law is that it is written down in a neat set of statutes in one large volume. Nothing could be further from the truth. The "law" comes from many different sources and a great deal of it is inferred from interpretive decisions made by judges and administrative hearing officers.

Society is becoming increasingly complex and increasingly dependent on the law. As a result, supervisors are learning that performing their routine duties can have a significant legal impact on both themselves and the organization in which they are involved. Hence, anyone functioning in a supervisory and/or administrative capacity must have a basic knowledge of the law. This knowledge includes a general understanding of the law as a whole, and a more specific knowledge of the legal areas that have a direct impact on them and the department.

The fire service is not immune from this ever-expanding trend toward legal dependency. The company officer functions in an environment where the need for quick thinking and fast action must be balanced with the prospect of possible exposure, both personally and organizationally, to legal liability (Figure 15.1 on next page). More fire departments, as governmental entities or private organizations, are confronted with lawsuits ranging from the disenchanted employee to the individual seeking to impose civil liability on the organization.

GENERAL PRINCIPLES OF ADMINISTRATIVE LAW

It is often said that the administrative process of modern government actually constitutes a fourth branch of government and one that is not to be found or defined in the Constitution.

Figure 15.1 Because company officers can be held liable for their actions, they may be required to testify in court.

The United States Constitution sets up a tripartite division of the federal government into legislative, executive, and judicial departments (Figure 15.2). This is complemented by a system of checks and balances between each branch. However, principally during the past 50 years, another component of government has grown dramatically. This is the great mass of agencies and resulting laws and guidelines referred to as administrative law.

The administrative law process has a significant impact on all members of society in general, and on the fire service in particular. There are literally hundreds of administrative agencies and thousands of agency-made laws that have a potential impact on the fire service manager. These range from employee/employer relations to the transportation of hazardous materials and every conceivable area in between. The effective manager must have a cursory knowledge of the administrative process and a working knowledge of the significant areas that impact the fire service.

The root of all agency power is the respective legislative or executive branch of government that creates the agency. This process of delegation has evolved over the years by necessity, partly because of the sheer volume of legislative work and partly through a need to incorporate needed technical expertise into legislation.

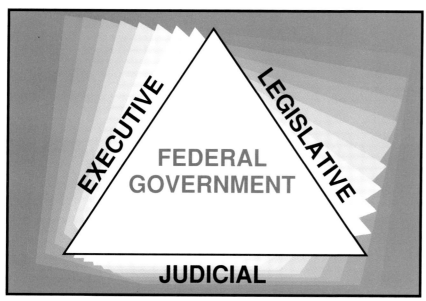

Figure 15.2 The federal government is divided into three parts: legislation, executive, and judicial departments.

Agencies are also given the authority to enforce the laws they make. This is accomplished through the establishment of an internal procedure within the agency. This procedure usually includes guidelines for enforcement of compliance, a hearing or review procedure, and the means to fine or punish offenders (Figure 15.3).

The practical effect of the growth of federal agency power is a host of agencies with the authority to make laws and the

Figure 15.3 A fine may be imposed for failure to adhere to fire laws within the jurisdiction.

power to compel compliance. The significance of this process is that appointed or delegated bodies can make laws, yet are not directly responsible to the voters.

It should be noted that respective states and provinces also have a host of agencies, also charged by the legislatures' and/or governors' offices with lawmaking. The state and provincial procedures closely parallel the federal procedure.

LEGAL DUTY AND LIABILITY

The great bulk of United States and Canadian law has its roots in the English Common Law. The adaptation carried some good and some bad legal concepts during the transition. The doctrine of sovereign immunity stems from the personal position of the English king, and basically means "A sovereign is exempt from suit, not because of any formal conception or obsolete theory, but on the logical and practical ground that there can be no legal right as against the authority that makes the law on which the right depends."

The Common Law doctrine carried over to U.S. and Canadian law and had the effect of holding any federal, state, or local government body immune from liability in tort (a tort is a civil wrong or injury). The practical effect was that any government body or agency, or employee thereof, was immune from liability for any action taken, negligent or otherwise, in an official capacity. For example, under the Common Law, a fire department and/or its officers would be immune from liability for running over a pedestrian in a crosswalk, even when such an act would normally be clearly negligent under statutory law. The doctrine protected the government from liability in all cases and often worked a hardship on citizens as a result.

In 1946, the United States Government waived its immunity from liability in tort and provided for the litigation of tort claims in the federal courts. Until recently, most states were immune from suits for tortious injury to persons or property. In the past few decades, however, the doctrine of sovereign immunity has undergone considerable erosion, legislative modification, and, in some cases, outright abolition by judicial decisions. Several mechanisms have been established that reflect the prevailing opinion that a government entity should assume some responsibility for the negligence of its agents and employees.

Most states have modified their Common Law immunity in one of the following ways:

- Doctrine of immunity still in force (but threatened)
- Limited liability by means of a tort claims act
  - Suits may be instituted as prescribed by statute
  - Suits brought before a special tribunal
  - Suits authorized only within prescribed limits

- Legislative claims boards
- Abandonment of immunity
  —Remedy is left to the courts as if the state were a private citizen

The situation is changing rapidly with respect to states' immunity in tort. In one state, for example, the legislature was informed that if it did not enact comprehensive tort claims procedures in the near future, the doctrine of immunity would be abrogated by the state supreme court. In other states, the concept of sovereign immunity has been declared unconstitutional.

The immunity situation for local jurisdictions, such as counties, cities, and towns, differs somewhat because of variations in state law. In some instances, immunity is afforded to local jurisdictions on the basis that it is derived directly from the state. Traditionally, some immunity from tort liability exists for those functions that are government in nature. Some incorporated municipalities, on the other hand, are fully responsible for their tortious acts, just as any other corporation would be. Basically, local jurisdictions have been more vulnerable than the states. Furthermore, when a state loses its immunity, its local jurisdictions lose theirs as well.

It is important to note that not only can a government agency now be held liable in tort, but an individual employee may also be liable. This type of situation is somewhat rare; it usually only occurs when someone commits an act on the job that is so much at variance with his or her training and expertise as to constitute gross negligence. In this case, a plaintiff would have to show that the employee had performed with complete disregard for his or her training and the agency's standard operating procedures. In several recent cases, individual employees have been found liable under a punitive damages award, designed to actually punish the employee for such deviant behavior. In such an action, the government agency is precluded from paying the fine for the individual. Today, the continuing trend away from sovereign immunity is clear, and tort and/or negligence liability exists in all but a few jurisdictions.

BASES FOR LEGAL ACTIONS

Tort Liability

A tort is a civil wrong or injury. The main purpose of a tort action is to seek payment for damages to property and injuries to individuals. The following elements must exist for a valid tort action:

- The defendant must owe a legal duty to the plaintiff.
- There must be a breach of duty; that is, the defendant must have failed to perform or to properly perform that duty.

- The breach of duty must be a proximate cause of the accident or injury that resulted.

- The plaintiff must have suffered damages as a result.

The first element, the matter of duty, is relatively easy to establish in a fire department related tort, as those having jurisdiction over the suppression, prevention, and related activities of a fire scene. Duty is also relatively clear with regard to the rendering of medical aid. The currently expanding area of hazardous materials may present more of a problem until the various jurisdictional responsibilities of the many agencies involved are settled.

The fact that the plaintiff has suffered damages is also readily established in accident cases. For example, damages may take the form of property repairs or replacement, medical expenses, or lost income (Figure 15.4). The dollar value of damages suffered, however, is an issue that may involve a considerable portion of a court proceeding.

Figure 15.4 Damages may include replacement value of the entire building and property.

Causation

The question of causation is more difficult to establish. A proximate cause is one that in a naturally continuous sequence produces the injury, and without which the result would not have occurred.

Note that breach of duty does not have to be the only cause; in fact, most accidents are the result of multiple factors. The proximate cause issue may be downplayed by a jury where the injuries are substantial or emotion laden, such as when a child is badly injured. When a jury is searching for a "deep pocket," (the litigants with the most money) they may be satisfied with a minimal linkage, negating the proximate cause criterion. For example, it may be sufficient in some instances to show that the procedure employed was not in accord with acceptable agency standards.

Negligence

The second element of a tort—breach of a legal duty—is the major issue in most tort liability cases. Negligence is the failure to exercise such care as a reasonable, prudent, and careful person would use under the same or similar circumstances. If the person possesses a greater amount of expertise, then his or her duty is proportionately greater. For instance, the standard of care for a fire officer would be that which a reasonable, prudent, and careful fire officer would be expected to possess.

The essence of negligence is the adequacy of performance. There are two ways in which one can be judged negligent: wrongful performance (misfeasance), or the omission of performance when some act should have been performed and was not (nonfeasance).

Standard Of Care

The critical issue in liability is the care with which the fire officer's responsibilities are exercised. If conduct falls below a reasonable standard of care, then the responsible persons and/or organizations may be held liable for injuries and damages that resulted from such conduct.

There are factors that may limit one's ability to act. One has a responsibility to act in a manner that is reasonable, based on the information at hand and the resources available (Figure 15.5). When a potentially hazardous condition exists, the reason-

Figure 15.5 A tenant of a building on fire may not understand the logic when choosing a defensive strategy.

ableness of action must take into account the following factors, particularly when resources are not available to correct all such conditions:

- Gravity of harm posed by the condition
- Likelihood of harm
- Availability of a method and/or equipment to correct the situation
- Usefulness of the condition for other purposes
- Burden of removing the condition

Many items of information may be brought into the court to aid in establishing the prevailing standard of care. One of the strongest types of evidence will be the agency's own guidelines and policies. Regulations adopted by the agency may define in detail the minimum requirements. A reasonable person would follow such rules and orders. Other sources of information bearing on the standard of care include:

- Agency directives and policies
- Directives of a superior agency (such as federal/state or province/local agency)
- Guidelines and policies of other agencies (to demonstrate accepted standards)
- Guidelines developed by national and professional organizations (such as the International Fire Service Training Association and the National Fire Protection Association)
- Professional texts and manuals
- Professional journals
- Research publications
- Opinions of expert witnesses

Personal Liability

The duty owed to the public for reasonably safe care extends to all parties responsible for abating hazardous situations and delivering emergency care. This includes individual employees of public agencies and private contractors. Basically, all individuals have the obligation to conduct themselves in a manner that does not negligently cause harm or further injure any other person. An individual who violates this general duty of care can be sued for damages.

If a court or jury decides that an individual is liable, then a judgment of damages can be returned against the individual. Recovery of punitive or exemplary damages is one reason for suing an individual employee, especially when the public agency is immune from paying such damages. From a practical standpoint, however, employees, particularly government employees, are not often held responsible for payment of awards. Because an individual's assets are small compared to those of the government, the "deeper pockets" will most likely be targeted for recovery of damages. Nevertheless, being named as a defendant in a lawsuit is a serious experience.

Supervisor's Responsibility For Subordinate's Acts

As a general rule, a supervisor is not responsible for the tortious acts of subordinates. There would be responsibility only if the supervisor had participated in the tortious conduct or had not exercised due care in selecting or supervising the subordinate.

There is often a concern about the situation that arises when one is instructed to do something that could create a dangerous condition. The courts have held that acting under orders is a good defense in this situation. From a practical standpoint, to hold subordinates responsible when working under orders would be unmanageable and unfair. In extreme cases, however, it may be the duty of a person acting under orders to attempt to mitigate a dangerous condition and to bring the hazard to the attention of superiors.

SUMMARY

The ever-increasing number of lawsuits makes it imperative company officers be knowledgeable about the law-making process, and about the legislative bodies that govern their municipality and state. Immunity from tort liability exists for those functions that are governmental in nature. Some incorporated municipalities are fully responsible for their tortious acts, just as any other corporation would be.

If a plaintiff has the four elements for tort prosecution, then the company officer personally and/or the municipality may be held liable. Although the situation is rare, the company officer may also be charged for the actions of a subordinate, if he or she is acting under the orders of the company officer.

Because of the seriousness of litigation, company officers must thoroughly understand their responsibilities and the direct impact prosecution could have on their position and on the department.

SUPPLEMENTAL READINGS

Bahme, Charles W. *Fire Service and the Law.* Boston: National Fire Protection Association, 1976.

Effective Supervisory Practices. 2nd ed. Washington D.C.: International City Management Association, 1984.

Management in the Fire Service. Didactic Systems, Inc. Boston: National Fire Protection Association, 1977.

Appendix A

Skills and Personnel Management Model
By Jack A. Treasure, Specialist
Fire and Rescue Training Institute
University of Missouri-Columbia

Society has created numerous products and procedures in the last decade or two that dramatically increase the hazards for firefighters at everyday calls. We cannot afford to approach these hazards without proper training and guidance, which jeopardizes our most vulnerable resource, the firefighter.

The following skills and personnel management model is offered to those volunteer and small, paid fire departments that do not have a structured career progression policy. There may be steps or phases that will not apply to your department, but in general, they can be a basis for creating a process that will help your organization (Figure A.1).

Each organization has an obligation to share with its members what is required to advance within that profession. It also must maintain records reflecting the training responsibilities the member has experienced if he or she chooses to apply to another department. What better testimony about our department can we have than members who qualify for better positions?

An attempt should be made to screen applicants who have problems or traits that could be detrimental to the fire service such as chronic alcoholism, mental deficiency or a physical im-

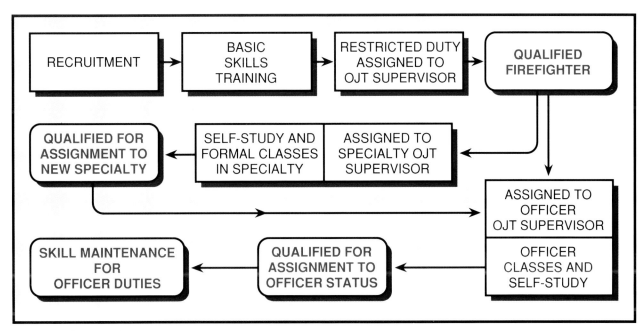

Figure A.1 This model illustrates the sequence of events needed for positive personnel development.

pairment that could be dangerous during an emergency situation. This is not to say that many of these people cannot help the organization in some manner, but they should be restricted from certain activities and told this from the beginning. We want our fire departments to be free and open societies and equal opportunity organizations, but we also have an obligation to screen out applicants who could cause harm to themselves or other firefighters. The criteria needs to be in writing to protect the department legally.

The days are gone where we can take all applicants, hand them emergency lights for their cars and a little protective gear, and christen them firefighters. Advancements in society and building materials during the last decades have caused everyday fires to become life-threatening to the firefighter. Now, it is imperative that the modern firefighters are armed with basic knowledge and skills prior to being placed in an environment that can kill them if they do not recognize the warning signals. At this point, many states permit fire departments to determine their own criteria for basic skills, but that may change in the not-too-distant future if we do not start regulating ourselves better.

Criteria we may identify as basic skills and knowledge should have a central theme of fire safety. Topics should include items identified in NFPA 1001: *Firefighter Professional Qualifications*. Special attention should be given to fire behavior, the need for and proper use of self-contained breathing apparatus, safe practices including emergency driving, recognition of hazardous materials and building collapse indications. Also, basic medical and rescue training should be presented.

Recruits should not be permitted to get involved with actual firefighting until they have completed basic skill training.

Upon completion, firefighter candidates should be placed on restricted duty and assigned to an on-job-training (OJT) supervisor. Restricted duty status means they cannot fight fire actively except when accompanied by their OJT supervisor.

The firefighter candidates should have turn-out gear (helmets and coats) that is color-coded for easy recognition by other members to prevent ordering candidates to do something for which they are not qualified. In the heat of the battle, it is tempting to order the nearest yellow coat to do something without knowing who is in that coat. Consideration could be given to assigning candidates the same radio number or roster number as the OJT supervisor with an added letter (A,B,C,) until the candidate becomes fully qualified. This helps to identify quickly who is responsible for that candidate on the fire scene.

On-the-job status means the OJT supervisor will have a candidate nearby during fireground operations, explaining what is happening. This allows the candidate to get hands-on experience without the additional risk of doing it alone. It will be the OJT supervisor's responsibility to see that the candidate gets the experience called for in the standardized recruit records.

At the completion of an emergency run, the OJT supervisor and candidate should critique the scene, and talk about what was good or bad about their role and the scene as a whole. The OJT supervisor should enter any new procedures experienced by the candidate in the OJT records. The candidate should initial the records, indicating an understanding of the material.

Perhaps this step is the most important part of the career process. At this point, a good potential firefighter can learn the proper attitude and goal identification to become either an exceptional firefighter or lazy and only do what is required. The OJT supervisor will have a great influence on the path the firefighter will take. Therefore, it is important which of your firefighters are selected to be OJT supervisors.

The OJT supervisors in the department should have a mastery of the basic skills of firefighting, a desire to pass these skills on to a recruit and should be progressive in nature and motivated to use the latest techniques.

After the selection of OJT supervisor personnel, an initial training session should be held, familiarizing them with their duties. This session should stress the need for proper record keeping and include the forms which will be used. The unit training officer normally would be the supervisor of the OJT process and, therefore, should be the one to direct their activities in the relationships with their assigned recruit.

The training officer and the OJT supervisors should hold monthly sessions, reviewing the progress of the recruits and to help motivate each other when it seems that none of their efforts are working.

If our criteria is correct, we now have firefighters who are qualified to perform on their own without direct supervision. They should know how to estimate what a fire is going to do, where to attack it and how to protect themselves in the process. They should have the rudimentary skills for effecting rescue. They should have a good understanding of the guidelines for emergency response driving, even if they are not eligible to drive a fire department vehicle immediately.

During this phase of the firefighters' careers, they should be encouraged and occasionally rewarded for honing skills and increasing their knowledge and effectiveness. Firefighters should have a choice, from this phase through the rest of their careers, to stay at this phase or to strive to progress in responsibility and duty assignments. There is nothing wrong if the firefighter elects to stay at this level as long as it is not an indication of stagnation and the firefighter continues to improve his or her abilities. After all, not everyone can become an officer and it probably is at this level that a person gets his or her greatest feeling of accomplishment for having done a job well.

After a period of time, if firefighters exhibit good potential for specialty training and are interested in doing that activity, they can be entered into the next phase.

Specialized training includes any items outside normal firefighting duty. Depending on the structure of your organization, the specialized areas could include: driver and pump operator, ladder operations, rescue team, medical team, fire cause determination, community fire prevention programs, equipment maintenance, training, public relations and communications.

It is vital to ensure that the firefighter does not perform one of these specialized areas without proper preparation and training. Proper training should include meeting the NFPA standards for that specialty, such as NFPA Standard 1002 for fire apparatus driver/operator qualification, Standard 1031 for fire inspector, investigator, prevention education officer qualification or Standard 1041 for fire service instructor qualification. The firefighter may find during this training that the job is not what he or she expected and should be able to discontinue without any further loss or effort by either party.

The firefighter should begin a two-fold learning process and be assigned to a specialty OJT supervisor. The firefighter should not be assigned to new duty at this point but officially entered in the training program for that duty.

For example, if the desired specialty training is as a pump operator, whenever the firefighter can be spared from duties on the fire scene, he or she should report to the specialty OJT supervisor (pump operator) where the functions of the pump operations can be observed. It may be necessary for the chief officers to help the training officer with the indoctrination session, so the specialty OJT supervisor is reassured that he or she is not training someone who is going to take the job away.

Concurrently, the firefighter should be directed to self-study materials such as the International Fire Service Training Association (IFSTA) manuals for that specialty and the required formal classes should be identified. State training schedules and other training sources should be reviewed to determine well in advance when the firefighter may attend the required classes.

If the firefighter wants to train in an area that is not performed in a department, it may be necessary for the administration and the training officer to do some research to determine the qualifications for the new specialty. A good basis will be the

NFPA standards and the IFSTA manuals, plus discussion with the state training coordinators.

After firefighters complete the required training and the functions identified in the OJT records, they can be carried as eligible for promotion to that specialty when an opening or need occurs. Periodic skill reviews and updates should be scheduled for skill maintenance during the waiting period.

Whether in a specialty or at firefighter status, any firefighter exhibiting leadership ability can be considered for entry into the Officer OJT Program.

Before consideration, the firefighter should have spent sufficient time in the fire service and have a track record that proves a knowledge and aptitude for firefighting. However, these facts alone do not prove he has leadership ability or that he would make a good officer. Many good firefighters have been promoted to an officer position, only to find it was not in their best interest. When the feeling of pride and prestige wears thin from making the necessary but unpopular decisions, the officer secretly may wish he or she were back fighting the fire with a nozzle rather than with strategy and tactics.

Still other officers have been lost because they could never come to terms with the feeling of importance and power that results from being promoted over other candidates. That feeling may be exhibited as an overbearing manner or a tendency to scream and holler when the situation does not warrant it. Whatever the manifestation, the results usually are that the officer has problems with the personnel under his command. This, too, can lead to the loss of a good firefighter or other large headaches for the administration.

Therefore, the administration must establish criteria for the officer recruiting and screening process that will serve and protect both parties. The time and energy spent carefully establishing the program can save countless problems later. None of us want to lose potentially good officers, nor do we want to lose good firefighters.

The Officer Development Program should include study that centers on the functions of management, since fire officers of all ranks perform as managers to some degree. The course of study should include the NFPA Standard 1021 for fire officer professional qualifications. The IFSTA manual **Fire Department Company Officer,** explains the supervisory functions of planning, organizing, staffing, directing and controlling. It also looks at leadership style and theory, as well as other dimensions of leadership. The IFSTA manual, **Chief Officer,** also is a good reference for study, covering such topics as planning, hiring practices, staffing, labor relations, information management, budgeting, emergency medical services, communication systems, safety and political activity. These help satisfy the six levels required in the NFPA Standard 1021. The program can be enhanced by the inclusion of formal classes offered by your state fire training agency and the National Fire Academy.

Again, the selection of the officer OJT supervisors must be made carefully. For the most part, they will come from the lower-ranking officers in our chain-of-command structure because that is the position the firefighter is striving for. We must ensure that the supervisor has not developed bad habits or attitudes throughout the years. We would not want the wrong traits passed along to the officer candidate.

Upon completing the Officer Development Program, the candidate's records should reflect eligibility for promotion. They should receive added credit for the additional self-study done at this point. College course work and degree programs would be examples, along with specialized management and leadership schools.

It is easy to assume that once a person is serving as an officer, she need not worry about taking classes or upgrading training. This could not be further from the truth. Skill maintenance plateaus must be established.

How many times have you heard, or said to yourself, that the department will be great when all of the old timers retire because they do not want to change anything? The problem seems to be that the younger members are attending classes and learning new techniques they would like to implement, while older members tend to say, "We have been doing things this way for years and it works fine, why change?"

If the administration required that all officers, as well as administrators, continue to take classes to upgrade training, it tends to narrow the gap between the thinking of the older and younger members.

This skills and personnel management model will not solve all of the management problems within a department. However, if it is used as a reference for building a structured progression table for your department, then perhaps it will remove the pesky question of "Where are we headed?"

Index

A

Accountability
  centralized, 32
  in chain of command, 12
  for decentralized decisions, 34
Achievement needs, firefighters', 135-137
Administrative law, 255-258
Adult ego state, 78
Adult-to-adult transaction, 79
Affiliation needs, firefighters', 135-136, 138
Alarm assignments, 201, 222
Alarm information, 205, 215
Authority
  centralized, 32
  decentralized, 31-34
  delegating, 18-19, 32, 34, 116-118
  overlapping, 28-32

B

Behavior
  expectations affecting, 130, 133
  human needs affecting, 135
  goal-oriented, 161
  group, 68
  modification, 152, 154, 159-160
  moral and ethical influences on, 130-132
  motivation, and, 131
  perspectives affecting, 132-133
  positive and negative, 131
  reinforcement, 151-152
  in social structure, 34
  standards of, 153
  unsatisfactory, 153
Benefit packages, 75
Bias. *See* Prejudice
Bonding, in fire company, 93
Breach
  of command, 14-16
  of departmental policy, 48
Brunacini, Alan, 109, 201, 227
Budgeting
  controls, 113-114
  justifying, 112-113
  planning tool, 111
  preliminary, 112

  process, 112-113
  proposed package, 112
Bulletins, 48, 63
Bureaucratic leadership style, 95-96

C

Career counseling, 7, 144
Certificate of achievement, 77
Chain of command, 13
  breaches in, 14-16
  in communication, 14
  fire chief in, 12
  firefighters' problems, and, 16
  one-supervisor principle, 12
  in scalar structure, 25-27
  in staff advisory system, 28
Child ego state, 78
Child-to-child transaction, 79-80
Civilians, in fire department, 28
Class, socioeconomic, 81-84
Coercive power, 99-101, 103-104
Command, unity of. *See* Unity of command
Command assignment, 210
Command system, incident. *See*
  Incident command and communication system
Communication
  barriers to, 43-44, 46
  empathy in, 46
  fireground, 49-51
  formal, 47
  informal, 52-53
  listening in, 45-46, 159
  medium, 43-45
  message, 43
  non-verbal, 44
  radio, 44, 228-230
  sender and receiver, 41-43, 234
  in transactional analysis, 78
Communication, face-to-face
  emotional states, and, 53
  evaluation interview, 158-160
  physical barriers to, 54
  relationships, and, 51
  selective hearing in, 52
  word meaning in, 52-53

Communication, written, 44-45
  business communication course, 61
  fireground, 50
  forms, 54-55
  letter, 54-58
  memorandum, 54
  reports, 59-61
Communications system, incident. *See* Incident
  command and communications system
Community services division, 19
Company officer
  career counselor, 7, 144
  communication skills, 45-46, 61, 158-159
  confidence, 230, 232
  fireground experience, 207
  leadership ability, 98-99
  leadership style, 98
  legal liability, 255
  middle manager, 109
  motivational skills, 129, 135
  orders, issuing, 49, 230-232
  problem solving skills, 167
  role in group, 72-73, 75
  success, achieving, 5-7
  time planning, 115-118
  transactional analysis, and, 80
  written policies, and, 47
Complaints, handling, 174-176
Complementary transactions, 79-80
Conflicts, confronting, 102-103
Construction considerations, 219, 221-222
Construction theory, 187, 222
Critical incident stress
  counseling, 259
  debriefing, 248-249
  "macho" image, and, 246
  peer support, 248
  reducing, 247
  symptoms, 245
  training, 247-248
Crossed transactions, 80
Cross training, 21

D
Decisions
  decentralized, 34
  policy as guide to, 46
Demotion, 157

Departmental services division, 19
Department policy manual, 47
Directives, 48-49
Discipline
  demotion, 157
  documentation, 157-158
  organizational, 21
  reprimand, oral, 155-156
  reprimand, written, 156
  rules and regulations as, 21
  suspension, 157
  termination, 157
  transfer, 156
Discrimination
  within fire company, 83-84
  racial, 81
  out-group, 82-83
Dispatcher, 230, 233
Division of labor, 19-21
Drawings, facility survey, 192-194
Drills, practice, 204
Dual-issue leadership style, 97

E
Ego fulfillment, 75, 77
Ego states, 78
Emergency response, 25, 48
Emergency services division, 19-21
Empathy, 46
Environment
  for listening, 46
  size-up consideration, 215-218
Equal opportunity employment, 47
Equipment requirements, fireground, 222-223
Ethnic minority groups, 83
Evaluation, employee
  alignment of company and individual, 144-145,
    151, 154
  behavior modification, and, 152-154, 159-160
  behavior reinforcement, and, 151-152
  of compatibility, 149-150
  criteria, 145, 154-155
  cycle, 150
  dialogue, 151
  documentation, 158
  fire service standards, and, 146-148
  formal, 145, 158
  informal, 145

of interaction, 150
interview, 158-160
of safety performance, 148-150
of skills, 143-144, 153
solutions, finding, 160
See also Discipline
Evaluation, operation, 120-121
Expenses, fixed, recurring, 112
Expert power, 10, 99, 101-104
Exposure protection, 188-189, 202, 205, 207
Extinguishing agent size-up, 223

F
Facilities, physical, 115
Facility survey policy, 182
Fair Labor Standards Act, 47
Field sketch, 192
Fire code enforcement survey, 183, 200
Fire Command, 201, 227
Fire company
discipline, 21
discrimination in, 83-84
division of labor, 19-21
organizational structure, 34-37
personality, 34-35
span of control, 17-19
unity, 11, 93
Fire confinement, 205
Fire department goals. *See* Goals,
fire department
Fire department organizational structures, 25-27.
See also Line and staff sections of fire department
Fire extinguishment, 205, 207
Firefighters
achievement needs of, 135-137
bonding, 93
in chain of command, 16
common interests of, 69
expectations of, fulfilling, 150
job satisfaction, 100
listening to, 16
officers, and, 51
problems of, 16
skills of, 43-45
strong, feeling, 99-100
teams of, 20
See also Injuries, firefighter; Stress,
firefighters'

Fireground
alarm assignments, 201
command assignment, 210
communications, 44, 49-51
company officer, role of, 199-200, 207
discipline, 227
exposure protection, 202, 205
fire attack, 201-202
goal, 199
hazardous materials, 207
hazard recognition, 199-200
monitoring, 210
operational strategies and tactics, 205-210
orders, 49, 230-231
priorities, 207
scalar organization, 35
report, initial, 208
responses, range of, 201
resource information, 200-201, 209
standard operating procedures, 203-204
strategic plans, 199-201, 204-205
tactical assignments, 210
training for, 204
See also Size-up; Incident command and
communications system
Fire loss, controlling, 27-28
Fire prevention, 59, 223
Fire protection engineer, 189, 222
Fire service
civilians in, 28
succeeding in, 5-7
Flat centralized organizational structure, 35
Forms, 54-55

G
General Adaptation Syndrome (GAS), 240-241
Goal oriented thinking, 103
Goals, fire department
controlling fire loss, 27-28
cooperation to achieve, 101
discipline for achieving, 21
expanding, 28
of formal and informal groups, 68, 76, 101-102
motivation to achieve, 69, 129, 130, 135
written, 67
Goal-setting process, 122-124
Grapevine, 61-63
Gratz, David B., 112

Group, formal
  fire company as, 67
  informal group influence, 67-68
  leader of, 71, 89
  rules and guidelines in, 73
Group, informal
  within formal group, 67-68
  interaction of members, 75
  leader of, 71
  rules and guidelines in, 73
Group dynamics
  common goals, 101-102
  common interests, 169
  influence on individual, 75
  interaction of members, 73, 75-76, 78
  leadership, 72-73
  group image, and, 76-77
  moral values, 70-71
  mutual trust, 100
  overachievers, and, 96
  positive self-image, and, 70
  rules and guidelines, 73
  sense of continuity, 70
  socioeconomic backgrounds in, 81-84
  traditional values, 71

H
Hazardous materials
  federal standards for, 47
  on fireground, 207
  size-up consideration, 219
  toxic vapors from, 216
  teams, 21
  technical assistance, 223
Hidden transactions, 80
Hierarchy of Needs, 74, 76
Human needs, 135-136
Human resources
  managers, 27
  organizing, 115
Human Side of Enterprise, The, 89

I
Identification power, 99, 101, 104
Incident command and communication system
  command, establishing, 227-228
  communication, control of, 233
  communication options, 233

dispatcher, 230, 233
first-arriving units, 227
management skills, 228
orders, 230-231
radio communications, 228-230
span of control, 17, 227
standard operating procedures, 227-228, 233
Incident scene. *See* Fireground
Information flow
  grapevine, 61-63
  official, 63
  in scalar structure, 27, 35-36
  in staff advisory system, 28
In-groups, 82
Injuries, civilian, 59
Injuries, firefighter
  National Fire Protection Association standard,
   237-238
  reducing, 240
  sources of, 238-239
Insubordination, 48
Interaction
  in circular organizational structure, 36
  in evaluation cycle, 150
  of group members, 73, 76, 78, 81
International Fire Service Training
  Association, 109
Interview, evaluation, 158-160
Investigation reports, 59

J
Job assignments, 12, 20
Job descriptions, 11, 20, 76
Job-related performance evaluation, 145
Job satisfaction, 100
Job security, 95

L
Labor-generated conflicts, 70
Layman, Loyd, 215
Leadership
  change in, 70
  common sense, 89
  confronting conflicts, 102-103
  cooperation, encouraging, 101-102
  by example, 21, 89
  of group, formal, 71, 81-82, 89
  of group, informal, 71-72

strength, building others', 99-100
trust, inspiring, 100-101
See also Theory X and Theory Y; Theory Z
Leadership styles, 95-97
Legitimate power, 101-103, 105
Letter writing, 55-58
Liability, company officer's, 255
  administrative law, 255-258
  damages, 260, 262-263
  personal, 262-263
  sovereign immunity, 258-259
  for subordinate, 263
  tort liability, 259-262
Life safety, 184-185, 207, 219
Line and staff sections of fire department, 27-28
  authority, overlapping, 28-32
  chain of command in, 28
  fire suppression, and, 28
  line advice to staff, 32
  staff advisory, 28-29
Listening skills, 16, 45-46, 159, 168

M
Mace, Harold, 109
Maintenance, 111
Management, elements of
  budgeting, 111-114
  cycle, 109-110
  directing and controlling, 119-120
  evaluating, 120-121
  goal-setting, 122-124
  implementing, 118
  organizing resources, 114-119
  planning, 110-111
Management model for volunteer and small fire
 departments, 265-270
Management by objectives, 114, 124-125
Maslow, Abraham, 74
Massey, Morris, 71
McGregor, Douglas, 89
Measurable objectives, 124-125, 160
Medical program, 249-250
Member assistance program, 249-250
Memorandum, 54, 63
Mental health professional, 248
Middle management, 14, 109
Middle-of-the-road leadership style, 97
Minorities, 83

Motivation
  behavior factor, 130, 135-136
  bureaucratic leadership style, and, 96
  company goals, and, 129-130
  feeling strong, and, 99
  organizational tasks as, 136-138
  single-issue leadership style, 96

N
National Fire Protection Association
  injury statistics, 239
  standards, 146-147, 237
Network of communications
  on fireground, 49-50
  social, 61
Non-verbal communication, 44

O
Objectives, measurable
  evaluation, 160
  management by, 124
  setting, 125
Officer-firefighter relationships, 51
Operational strategies, 205-209
Operational tactics, 205-206, 209-210
Orders
  definition, 48
  fireground, 49-51, 230-232
  issuing, 48-49
Organizational chart, 26
Organizational principles, 12
Organizational structures
  circular, 36-37
  flat centralized, 35
  at incident scene, 227
  scalar, 35-36
  social, 34-35
Ouchi, William, 93
Out-groups, 82
Overhaul, 205

P
Parent-to-child ego state, 79
Parent ego state, 78
Personality, company, 34-35
Personnel requirements at fireground, 223
Physical fitness, 237
  program, 249-250
  stress reduction, 243

Physiological needs, firefighters', 74
Policies, department
  on breaches of command, 15-16
  changes in, 70, 76
  on decision making authority, 34
  staff advisory system, and, 28
  unwritten, 47
  written, 46-47
Power needs, firefighters', 135-138
Power structures, 103
  coercive, 99-101, 103-104, 161
  expert, 99, 101-104
  identification, 99, 101, 104, 161
  legitimate, 101-103, 105, 161
Pre-incident facility survey
  codes and standards, 195
  Commercial Occupancy Assessment, 186
  company officer's role, 195
  construction, 187-188, 192
  definition, 182
  drawings, 192-194
  equipment, 190-191
  exposure protection, 188-189, 191
  exterior survey, 191
  hazards, defining, 185, 200
  interior survey, 191-192
  life safety concerns, 184-185
  owner/tenant information, 185, 187
  photography, use of, 194-195
  property conservation, 189-190
  public relations, and, 195
  security problems, 187
  systematic approach, 191
  as training, 182
  ventilation information, 188
  water supply, 188
Pre-incident planning
  definition, 181
  technical sources, 223
  as written communication, 44
Prejudice
  communication barrier, 46
  discrimination, and, 82-84
Problem resolution sequential method, 167
Problem solving
  alternatives, 170-171
  analyzing, 169-170
  collecting data, 168-169
  corrective action, 172-173

recognition, 168
  solutions, 171
  See also Complaints, handling
Productivity, 93, 96-97
Property conservation, 189-190, 207
Punishment
  coercive power, and, 104
  for inappropriate behavior, 34

Q
Questions
  close-ended, 168-169
  open-ended, 169, 174

R
Racial discrimination, 81
Reinforcement
  behavior, 151-152
  of group image, 77
  of self-image, 133
Report, fireground, 208
Reports, written, 59-61
Reprimands, 155-156
Rescue strategy, 205, 207
Resources
  firefighters' skills, 143-145
  human, 115
  organizing, 114-118
  physical facilities, 115
  time, 115-118
  training, 115
Reward
  for appropriate behavior, 34, 151
  power, 99-101, 103-104
Rules and regulations, written, 21

S
Safety, firefighters', 237
Safety, life, 184-185, 207, 219
Safety and security, firefighters' need for, 74
Salvage strategy, 205
Scalar structure, 25-27, 35-36
Selective hearing, 52
Self-actualization, 76, 96-97
Self-esteem, firefighters' need for, 75, 77-78, 96
Self-image
  altering, 133
  in group dynamics, 75, 77-78
Selye, Hans, 240

Shift changes, 70
Single-issue leadership style, 96-97
Size-up, 215-216
    collapse, potential, 219-220
    construction, 219, 221
    egress, 220
    equipment available, 222-223
    extinguishing agent, 222-223
    fire protection, built-in, 221
    forcible entry, 220
    hazardous materials, 219, 223
    initial dispatch, 218
    life safety factors, 219
    nature of incident, 218
    occupancy, 219-221
    personnel available, 222
    time of day, 218
    topography, 218
    ventilation, 221
    weather considerations, 215-218
Skills, firefighters', 143-144
"Skills and Personnel Management
    Model", 265-270
Social communications network, 61
Social needs of individual, 75
    fulfillment of, 76-77, 96
Social status in group, 81
Social structure, organizational, 34-35
Socioeconomic backgrounds of group members,
    81-84
Sovereign immunity, 258-259
Span of control, 17-19
    authority, delegating, 18-19
    at emergency scene, 17, 227
    number of people in, 17-18
    responsibility, assigning, 17
    scalar structure, and, 27
Specialization, 20-21
Staff advisory system
    direct implementation, 28-30
    overlap, 30-32
    traditional, 28
Staff section. *See* Line and staff sections of fire
    department
Stamp collecting, 81
Standard Operating Procedures (SOP)
    discipline for achieving goals, 21
    as evaluation criteria, 146-148
    on fireground, 203

    measurable standard, 48
    point of reference, 48
    revising, 76
    unity, and, 11
    as written communication, 44
    See also National Fire Protection Association
        standards
Stress, firefighters'
    chronic, 240-241
    physiological response, 241
    reducing, 242
    stressors, 241-242
    substance abuse, and, 244-245
    wellness programs, 249-250
    See also Critical incident stres
Strokes, positive and negative, 80-81
Substance abuse, 244-245
Supervisor, reporting to, 12, 26
Supplies, conserving, 111
Suspension, 157

T
Tactical assignments, 210
Tactics, operational, 205-206, 209-210
Technical assistance, size-up, 222-223
Termination, 157
Theory X and Theory Y
    leadership style, 98
    overview, 91-92
    premises, 90
    problems, 93
    in single-issue leadership, 96-97
    workers, concern for, 98
Theory Z
    overview, 94
    premises, 93
    problems, 93
    workers, concern for, 98
Time
    company officer's, 115-117
    firefighters', 117-118
Tradition, and policy making, 47
Training
    company officer's, 5-6
    pre-incident survey as, 182
    radio communication, 229
    to raise standards, 146
    resources, 115

specialization, 20-21
in standard operating procedures, 41, 204
Training aids, 44
Transactional Analysis
ego states, 78
stamp collecting, 81
strokes, 80-81
transactions, 79-80
Transfer, 156
Treasure, Jack A., 265
Trust, 100-101
Turnover rates, 96

U
Unity of command, 12-14
authority, overlapping, 30
breaches in, 14-16
chain of command in, 12-14
at incident scene, 227
one-supervisor principle, 12

V
Ventilation
construction feature, 221
operational strategy, 205
wind, and, 217
Volunteer and small fire departments,
management model for, 265-270
Wellness programs, 249-250
Wildfire, 216, 218
Writing skills, 55, 59, 61
Work assignment groupings, 19
Workers, concern for, 96-98

IFSTA MANUALS

FIRE SERVICE ORIENTATION & INDOCTRINATION

History, traditions, and organization of the fire service; operation of the fire department and responsibilities and duties of firefighters; fire department companies and their functions; glossary of fire service terms.

FIRE SERVICE FIRST RESPONDER

Covers all objectives for U.S. DOT First Responder Training Courses as well as NFPA 1001 Emergency Medical Care sections. The special emphasis on maintenance of the ABC's features updated CPR techniques. Also included are scene assessment and safety, patient assessment, shock, bleeding, control spinal injuries, burns, heat and cold emergencies, medical emergencies, poisons, behavioral emergencies, emergency childbirth, short-distance transfer, and emergency vehicles and their equipment.

ESSENTIALS OF FIRE FIGHTING

This manual was prepared to meet the objectives set forth in levels I and II of NFPA 1001, *Fire Fighter Professional Qualifications*. Included in the manual are the basics of fire behavior, extinguishers, ropes and knots, self-contained breathing apparatus, ladders, forcible entry, rescue, water supply, fire streams, hose, ventilation, salvage and overhaul, fire cause determination, fire suppression techniques, communications, sprinkler systems, and fire inspection.

SELF-INSTRUCTION FOR ESSENTIALS

Over 260 pages of structured questions and answers for studying the *Essentials of Fire Fighting*. Each unit begins with the NFPA Standard No. 1001 required performance objectives. This self-instruction book will help you to learn many of the important topics and review the basic text.

IFSTA'S 500 COMPETENCIES FOR FIREFIGHTER CERTIFICATION

This manual identifies the competencies that must be achieved for certification as a firefighter for levels I and II. The text also identifies what the instructor needs to give the student, NFPA standards, and has space to record the student's score, local standards, and the instructor's initials.

FIRE SERVICE GROUND LADDER PRACTICES

Various terms applied to ladders; types, construction, maintenance, and testing of fire service ground ladders; detailed information on handling ground ladders and special tasks related to them.

HOSE PRACTICES

This new edition has been updated to reflect the latest information on modern fire hose and couplings, including large diameter hose. Details basic methods for handling hose and coupling construction; care, maintenance, and testing; hose appliances and tools; basic methods of handling hose; supply and attack methods; special hose operations.

SALVAGE AND OVERHAUL PRACTICES

Planning and preparing for salvage operations, care and preparations of equipment, methods of spreading and folding salvage covers, most effective way to handle water runoff, value of proper overhaul and equipment needed, and recognizing and preserving arson evidence.

FORCIBLE ENTRY

This comprehensive manual contains technical information about forcible entry tactics; tools; and door, window, and wall construction. Forcible entry methods are described for door, window, and wall entry. A new section on locks and through-the-lock entry makes this the most up-to-date manual available for forcible entry training.

SELF-CONTAINED BREATHING APPARATUS

Beginning with the history of breathing apparatus and the reasons they are needed, to how to use them, including maintenance and care, the firefighter is taken step by step with the aid of programmed-learning questions and answers throughout to complete knowledge of the subject. The donning, operation, and care of all types of breathing apparatus are covered in depth, as are training in SCBA use breathing-air purification and recharging cylinders. There are also special chapters on emergency escape procedures and interior search and rescue.

FIRE VENTILATION PRACTICES

Objectives and advantages of ventilation; requirements for burning, flammable liquid characteristics and products of combustion; phases of burning, backdrafts, and the transmission of heat; construction features to be considered; the ventilation process including evaluating and size-up is discussed in length.

FIRE SERVICE RESCUE PRACTICES

Sections include water and ice rescue, trenching, cave rescue, rigging, search-and-rescue techniques for inside structures and outside, and taking command at an incident. Also included are vehicle extrication and a complete section on rescue tools. The book covers all the information called for by the rescue sections of NFPA 1001 for Fire Fighter I, II, and III, and is profusely illustrated.

HAZARDOUS MATERIALS FOR FIRST RESPONDERS

Designed to assist first-arriving companies in identification of hazardous materials and scene assessment. Covers initial scene control and operations to maintain safety for all responders. Includes characteristics of hazardous materials, identifying hazardous materials, pre-incident planning, personal protective equipment, command and control of incidents, operations at hazardous materials incidents, and control agents.

STUDY GUIDE FOR HAZARDOUS MATERIALS FOR FIRST RESPONDERS

Written to complement the *Hazardous Materials for First Responders* manual, this study guide allows students to review procedures and ensure they understand characteristics of hazardous materials, pre-incident planning, command, and on-scene tactics. Through the use of questions and answers, this study guide promotes retention of essential information. Included are case studies that simulate hazardous material situations and incidents.

THE FIRE DEPARTMENT COMPANY OFFICER

This manual focuses on the basic principles of fire department organization, working relationships, and personnel management. For the firefighter aspiring to become a company officer and the company officer who wishes to improve management skills, this manual will be invaluable. This manual will help individuals develop and improve the necessary traits to effectively manage the fire company.

FIRE CAUSE DETERMINATION

Covers need for determination, finding origin and cause, documenting evidence, interviewing witnesses, courtroom demeanor, and more. Ideal text for company officers, firefighters, inspectors, investigators, insurance and industrial personnel.

PRIVATE FIRE PROTECTION & DETECTION

Automatic sprinkler systems, special extinguishing systems, standpipes, detection and alarm systems. Includes how to test sprinkler systems for the firefighter to meet NFPA 1001.

INDUSTRIAL FIRE PROTECTION

Devastating fires in industrial plants occur at a rate of 145 fires every day. *Industrial Fire Protection* is the single source document designed for training and managing industrial fire brigades. A must for all industrial sites, large and small, to meet the requirements of the Occupational Safety and Health Administration's (OSHA) regulation 29 CFR part 1910, Subpart L, concerning incipient industrial fire fighting.

CHIEF OFFICER

The role of the fire service has expanded from solely fire suppression to include public education, emergency medical services, and hazardous materials control. This manual provides an overview of the skills needed by today's chief officer. Included are coordination of emergency medical services, master planning, disaster planning, budgeting, information management, labor relations, and the political process. Referenced where appropriate to NFPA 1021, *Fire Fighter Professional Qualifications*, for levels V and VI.

SI CHIEF OFFICER

This manual assists those reading the text in retaining the principles and concepts necessary to be a skilled chief officer. It includes structured questions and answers, exercises, and a new supplemental section on Resolution by Objectives. It will serve as a review of the text and assist in promotional exam preparation.

PUBLIC FIRE EDUCATION

Public fire education planning, target audiences, seasonal fire problems, smoke detectors, working with the media, burn injuries, and resource exchange.

FIRE INSPECTION AND CODE ENFORCEMENT

This revised edition is designed to serve as a reference and training manual for fire department inspection personnel. Includes authority and responsibility; inspection procedures; principles of fire protection and fire cause determination; building construction for fire and life safety; means of egress; extinguishing equipment and fire protection systems; plans review, storage, handling, and use of hazardous materials.

STUDY GUIDE FOR FIRE INSPECTION AND CODE ENFORCEMENT

The *Fire Inspection and Code Enforcement Study Guide* is designed to supplement the *Fire Inspection and Code Enforcement* manual by providing questions and answers to key areas addressed within the manual. This study guide can help the student obtain a thorough understanding of NFPA 1031, levels I and II. Included are case studies that simulate inspection responsibilities.

WATER SUPPLIES FOR FIRE PROTECTION

Designed to help improve understanding of the principles, requirements, and standards used to provide water for fire fighting. Revised (1987) to include information about rural water supplies. Includes water supply management, water system fundamentals, fire hydrants, fire flow testing, static sources, relay operations, and shuttle operations.

FIRE DEPARTMENT PUMPING APPARATUS

The driver/operator's encyclopedia on operating fire department pumps and pumping apparatus. Includes the driver/operator; operating emergency vehicles; types of pumping apparatus; positioning apparatus; fire pump theory; operating fire pumps; apparatus maintenance; apparatus testing; apparatus purchase and specifications. Also included are detailed appendices covering the operation of all major manufacturers' pumps.

STUDY GUIDE FOR FIRE DEPARTMENT PUMPING APPARATUS

This Study Guide is designed to supplement *Fire Department Pumping Apparatus*. It identifies important information and concepts by providing questions and answers developed directly from the manual. When properly used, it ensures a better understanding of driver/operator responsibilities and proficiency.

FIRE STREAM PRACTICES

Characteristics, requirements, and principles of fire streams; developing, computing, and applying various types of streams to operational situations; formulas for application of hydraulics; actions and reactions created by applying streams under different circumstances.

FIRE PROTECTION ADMINISTRATION

A reprint of the Illinois Department of Commerce and Community Affairs publication. A manual for trustees, municipal officials, and fire chiefs of fire districts and small communities. Subjects covered include officials' duties and responsibilities, organization and management, personnel management and training, budgeting and finance, annexation and disconnection.

BUILDING CONSTRUCTION

This 170-page manual covers building construction features vital to developing fire fighting tactics in a structure. Subjects include construction principles, assemblies and their fire resistance, building services, door and window assemblies and special types of structures.

FIREFIGHTER SAFETY

Basic concepts and philosophy of accident prevention; essentials of a safety program and training for safety; station house facility safety; hazards en route and at the emergency scene; personal protective equipment; special hazards, including chemicals, electricity, and radioactive materials; inspection safety; health considerations.

AIRCRAFT FIRE PROTECTION AND RESCUE PROCEDURES

Aircraft types, engines, and systems; conventional and specialized fire fighting apparatus, tools, clothing, extinguishing agents; dangerous materials; communications; pre-fire planning; and airfield operations.

GROUND COVER FIRE FIGHTING PRACTICES

Ground cover fire apparatus, equipment, extinguishing agents, and fireground safety; organization and planning for ground cover fire; authority, jurisdiction, and mutual aid; techniques and procedures used for combating ground cover fire.

INCIDENT COMMAND SYSTEM

Developed by a multi-agency task force, this manual is designed to be used by fire, police, and other government groups during an emergency. ICS is the approved basic command system as taught at the National Fire Academy. Includes components of ICS, major incident organization, and strike team kind/types and minimum standards.

LEADERSHIP FOR THE COMPANY OFFICER

A 12- to 15-hour course designed for the new company officer or the firefighter who anticipates promotion to company officer. Includes introduction to leadership, leadership techniques, theories of human motivation, determining leadership style, leadership styles, and demanding leadership situations.

FIRE SERVICE PRACTICES FOR VOLUNTEER AND SMALL COMMUNITY FIRE DEPARTMENTS

A general overview of material covered in detail in Forcible Entry, Ladders, Hose, Salvage and Overhaul, Fire Streams, Apparatus, Ventilation, Rescue, Inspection, Self-Contained Breathing Apparatus, and Public Fire Education.

PRINCIPLES OF EXTRICATION

This manual is designed for use by firefighters and emergency medical service personnel who respond to extrication emergencies. The text includes information on the organization and administration of a rescue company, taking charge and scene assessment, site management and incident command, rescue vehicles and equipment, personal protective equipment for rescuers, extrication from automobiles, extrication from buses, extrication and evacuation of passenger trains, agricultural extrication and rescue, and industrial extrication.

HAZ MAT LEAK & SPILL GUIDE

A brief, practical treatise that reviews operations at spills and leaks. Sample S.O.P. and command recommendations along with a decontamination guide.

TRANSPARENCIES

Multicolored overhead transparencies to augment *Essentials of Fire Fighting* and other texts. Since costs and availability vary with different chapters, contact IFSTA Headquarters for details.

SLIDES

2-inch by 2-inch slides that can be used in any 35 mm slide projector. Subjects include:

Sprinklers (4 modules)
Smoke Detectors Can Save Your Life
Matches Aren't For Children
Public Relations for the Fire Service
Public Fire Education Specialist (Slide/Tape)

FIREFIGHTER VIDEOTAPE SERIES

Designed to reinforce basic skills and increase knowledge on a variety of fire fighting topics. Excellent for use with *Essentials* or *Volunteer* to review and emphasize different topics. Available for Firefighter levels I, II, and III.

IFSTA BINDERS

Heavy-duty three-ring binders for organizing and protecting your IFSTA manuals. Available in two sizes: 1 1/2 inch and 3 inch.

WATER FLOW SUMMARY SHEETS

50 summary sheets and instructions for use; logarithmic scale to simplify the process of determining the available water in an area.

PERSONNEL RECORD FOLDERS

Personnel record folders should be used by the training officer for each member of the department. Such data as training, seminars, and college courses can be recorded, along with other valuable information. Letter or legal size.

ADDITIONAL PUBLICATIONS AND TRAINING MATERIALS ARE AVAILABLE, CALL FOR A FREE CATALOG.
Call Toll Free 1-800-654-4055 or FAX # 1-405-744-8204

SHIP TO: DATE: _____

NAME _____

CUSTOMER ACCOUNT NO: PHONE _____

STREET ADDRESS (Shipped UPS) _____

CITY   STATE   ZIP _____

SIGNATURE _____

SOCIAL SECURITY NO. OR FEDERAL ID NO. ___

(NOTE: Order cannot be processed without signature.)

☐ VISA   ☐ MASTERCARD   ☐ AMERICAN EXPRESS

CARD # _____ EXP. DATE _____

Payment Enclosed ☐   Bill Me Later ☐

ORDER FORM

ifsta ®

10/90

Send to:
Fire Protection Publications
Oklahoma State University
Stillwater, Oklahoma 74078-0118
1-800-654-4055
Or Contact Your Local Distributor

Allow 4 to 6 weeks for delivery.

FILL IN THE ITEMS AND QUANTITIES DESIRED

QUANTITY	TITLE	LIST PRICE	TOTAL

Orders **outside** United States, contact Customer Services for shipping and handling charges.

Obtain postage and prices from current IFSTA Catalog or they will be inserted by Customer Services.

NOTE: Payment with your order saves you postage and handling charges when ordering from Fire Protection Publications.

SUBTOTAL _____

Postage and Handling
if applicable _____

TOTAL _____

TOLL-FREE NUMBER
1-800-654-4055

FAX YOUR ORDER
1-405-744-8204

COMMENT SHEET

DATE _____ NAME _____

ADDRESS _____

ORGANIZATION REPRESENTED _____

CHAPTER TITLE _____ NUMBER _____

SECTION/PARAGRAPH/FIGURE _____ PAGE _____

1. Proposal (include proposed wording, or identification of wording to be deleted),
    OR PROPOSED FIGURE:

2. Statement of Problem and Substantiation for Proposal:

RETURN TO: IFSTA Editor   SIGNATURE _____
            Fire Protection Publications
            Oklahoma State University
            Stillwater, OK 74078

Use this sheet to make any suggestions, recommendations, or comments. We need your input to make the manuals the most up to date as possible. Your help is appreciated. Use additional pages if necessary.